MY SCARS ARE MY BIRTHMARK

ORLANDO TAYLOR

Absolute Author
Publishing House

My Scars Are My Birthmark

Copyright © 2021 by Orlando Taylor

For information contact:
otaylor@kuumbaconcepts.com

Publisher: Absolute Author Publishing House
Editor: Dr. Melissa Caudle
Associate Editor: Kathy Rabb Kittok
Cover Design: Orlando Taylor

ISBN: 978-1-64953-307-4

First Edition: August 2021

9 8 7 6 5 4 3 2 1

Table of Contents

Dedication

To my mother who gave me my passion for reading, words, and life. Truest example of love, even when her life felt unworthy and without notice from god as a African woman.

CHAPTER ONE

OSRAM NE NSOROMMA**

love, faithfulness, harmony

A Beautiful One

I need a beautiful one...
to help me forget childhood pains like
watching a soul sister running down the Vinegrove
set on fire, screaming in perfect harmony,
because her man set her ablaze in his fury's haze
to caress my skin with precious oils, soothing it from the sting
of life's acid rain,
and ease the sub-atomic pain running
at warp 9 speed through every corner of my mind.

I need a beautiful one...
to share the day and spend the night
with love and dedication in each hand,
working the tension out the muscles in my back
eating breakfast together before going our separate ways my
mind replays images of your burnt bronze face
to help me make it through the bullshit of the day.

I need a beautiful one...
to knock gently on my door when the walls of night are closing
in on me
suffocating from what the future holds,
my present, the past, ... from life itself sometimes
giving me the extra strength to see the ray in the next day.

Oh Lord, I pray you forgive me for
spitting on the day and cursing out the night,
that you would have mercy on me

as you did for those long ago

raining down manna to

quench the thirst of this
burden in the pit on my soul
someday, I pray soon, you will find me
worthy to possess a beautiful one...
but until the day rises, I shall be in prayer
on bruised knees in need of...
a beautiful one.

Share This Voyage

I need good friends
Ain't afraid to admit
If life dictates
Live without you
Smile without you
Cry without you
Fail without you
Laugh without you
Stand without you
Die without you
Succeed without you
Soar without you
not thinking about you
Jump in the fire without you
Surf the universe without you

WANTED good souls
No fees involved

love & action

For you I will pull back the heavens
see into the nineth dimension
Astral project your soul
to the four corners of the earth
so you can witness all beauty at once.
Crack the earth to its deepest core
warmth for the coldest winter.
Bring you water from the Nile
to quench your long diasporic journey.
Wade into the river's current,
Cleansing our doubts with each ripple's flow.
Sit on a hill under a grove of trees
birds singing life's symphony.
A note in a bottle to you
Swig of my verbal expressions
Intense emotions locked in my chest,
Come take a swallow of the best.
Stars forsake their natural place
With strength from the ancestors
I'll catch and return them black sea,
saving one to keep for you and me.

Orlando Taylor

Are You the One?

Are you the one whom I can trust?
Catch the tears of my pain
in the middle of your hand,
Allow me to lay my head
in the middle of your chest?
Or are you the one who makes me sit
in the middle of the floor
in darkness bathing myself
in the tears you created.

Are you the one who I will run
when I wear the blues?
Laugh about the silly things of the day
Hold hands, the embraces,
moist touch of our mouths
Or will you be the stone that falls upon me
crushing my spirit with deceit.

Are you the one causing the moon to shake
and the stars to fall in a shower of lights
all over my skin when we make love?
I have been born again
through the togetherness of our souls.
Or will you be the one
to make my soul feel old.

No More Passion

How is it that the person who swoons
from the heat of your presence,
give the moon wrapped in stars and ribbons of sun rays,
make you desperate for a space devoid of them?

How is it that the person who makes you feel safe,
like the womb you once thought was a part of you,
shelter no winter gale
or summer storm could prevail;
cause your heart to burst like 4th of July sparkles
chaos beyond mending?

How do tender lip's whispers
dancing across your skin
bringing your body shivering pleasures
spit so many verbs of hate?
Assail you with word's brutal billy club
shattering your self being.

Missing You

I miss you tomorrow and think of you each today
Laid my head heavily on my desk
Looked up at the picture of your face
Wish you were here so stars explode
dance with me in the rain of stardust.

I miss you turn the key and cross the threshold
Watching TV only one coaster
I see your toothbrush daily,
Silence on the phone, broken glass under my feet,
Crippling pain walking away.

Waking up in the morning
someone covered me with the night
A light I found when I was not lookingT
hat blinds my recall of yours.

Fruit

He was nothing I could have but all I wanted.
His love means my own destruction,
but we all must die.

His love engulfs my every thought
foaming cyanide's pain.
Yet I run after it even more.

He is everything I hate in a man.
Haughty eyes and lips curled in scorn
Shining eyes and menacing disposition
Threatening to his brothers without words.

I keep coming
he is the fruit that appears good
taste of his thoughts, smell of his presence
But etched into his geometric features
Death's angry dance peeks with defiance.

exhale too

men. no good sons of bitches
just like dogs,
looking for someone to piss on.
a good fuck
and they gone.
I'm looking for a real man.

that's all I ever hear.

who said you had the market
on broken hearts?
who said you were the only
one tired of lonely nights?
who said you're the only one
awake at night hoping
against the odds for a special someone?
someone who can make you laugh,
someone to console cries
tired of the games,
lies, the hiding of the caller i.d.
who said you're the only one heart hurts?
lovers holding hands
knowing each other's eyes.
I need a friend who listens to me
Not just hears me
build me up
so, we can support each other.
I'm waiting to exhale too.

st. louis blues

i woke up this monin' an' rolled ova
sheets next to me were cold
an' my babee was gwon
i woke up this hearya monin' and
foun' my babee gwon
what i'm gonna do with out my boo
all i know is my bed is cold
and i'm a man all alone
think i'm gonna buy me a nine
put a window in de middle
of my head to warm de
coldness in my bed
but befo' i do ma self
i'm gonna run down labadie ave
and fin' de house where he stay wid his
momma and put a whole where
he shot me.

Auset and Ausar

I am looking for my one
we have been separated for days.
oh, i guess that's a thousand centuries to you.

we were together before there were stars.
Space had no planets, no galaxies.
Dark saves the light we created
when we sat, touching each other.
Chased her about in the beautiful darkness
we laughed and played no cares.

We were children
I tripped over my feet one time
as we ran through the black space.
Auset laughed so hard tears ran off
her face and started dancing in the darkness
creating wonderful points of light.
She put her hand over mouth
Afraid what else would happen.
We walked and played for millennia
amongst those tears.
When we held hands for the first time,
threads of light started
racing and crisscrossing silently
about our bodies.
I called this lightning.
Auset and I are in love.

We made love
she was shy yet passionate

Caressed the crevice in my chest
and a planet was born.
Kissed the corners of my eyes
an explosion of nova light
fell from my eyes
it burned hot, yet soothing
she reached up
held it in her hand
she named it ra
Rotated around her
and rotated, and rotated until
my throat uttered a moan across multi-verse
She arched her back to me in a rainbow
fall
fell,
I, deeper, into her
waves of creation
with my phallic motions.

I heard a cry
I thought it was me
Auset mused as we held each other
passing through the warmth of the glow
heard a cry
Auset mused and looked down
it was our son heru.
The others called him man.

I am because she is, the first family.

Taboo

Come take my hand
down the hall to my room
close the door
don't turn on the light
sit in the dark
I see you in the moonlight
I like the way you feel
standing cheek to cheek, chest to chest
hand sprints up and down your legs
the smell of your warm breath intoxicates me
If anyone knew about our love
a furious commotion would ensue
rumors all around town
so close your heart and hide your mouth
in the warm shelter of mine
our love is so taboo.

Let's rendezvous 'round eight
keep quiet put your words in my hand
down by the creek, just you and I
watch the sun go down
set in red-orange
we'll laugh and tumble madly about the ground
afterword's pick the grass from our hair
hold each other one last time
to have a spare when we part

If anyone knew about our love
a furious commotion would be
rumors all around town
so close your heart and hide your mouth

in the warm shelter of mine
our love is so taboo
Upon the roof your projects
watch life pass in the city
talk about dreams and the future
beautiful you and I together
No power on earth can separate
amongst the constellations of heaven
written was our fate, but we must be careful
If anyone knew about our love
a furious commotion would be
rumors all around town close
so close your heart and hide your mouth
in the warm shelter of mine
our love is so taboo.

Home

Warm hugs my mother's arms
The aroma of love cooking
brothers and I crowded in one room
Talking, laughing under the moon
Shouting, arguing, maybe a fight
I found a corner sanctuary
Dodge-ball, double-dutch,
hide-n-go-seek Mother-may-I,
football, soccer, rock teacher
Running, screaming owning the streets
Soul rhythms blare from open windows
Screams from children ricochet like echoes
Tony got mad went home with his ball
Suffocating humidity and heat
Anger pops like water on hot grease
Violence strangles elder's wisdom
The neighborhood gentrification
Three burned homes prophesized
Black dreams and wealth cannibalized
Crips and Bloods invading aliens
Crack riddled the community
Like Sean Bell's body thirty police bullets
The country held their collective breath
'til white teens died using ecstasy and meth
We cried throwing dirt on young coffins
Poverty pecked at the marrow of my spirit
Hungry nights squeezed chest like asthma
Every hour looking for Ra's boat
Awaiting to be an adult.
Writing life's literary non-fiction
Brings perfect spiritual diction.

I forage for smiles in bitter eyes
Brothers sharing heavy laughter
Not destroying him with knuckled words
Sisters supporting their commonality
No jealous assassinations
Perfection only occurs in children's fantasies
Closed eyes touching blessed memories
Where I am from for many became a tomb
Shame does not mock me to call it home
A flower bursting from the soil
Nourished by the forgotten places
Stretching to the sun.

Soul mate (haiku)

Find a soul not a mate
Taste the world, enjoy nectar
The one comes later

Feelin's for You

Like a brothas rims when he stops,
my head keeps spinnin'
Intelligent without being complicated
spring days nurturing last year's seeds
children playing in a fire hydrant
Creating rainbows of hope
extending from the dusky asphalt
to the tops of old houses
Break the seal and take a swig,
damn you more than 80 proof
Bounce my communication
off heavenly satellites just
to get through to you.

When you are starvin'
Break off a piece of my soul
Eat last just to make sure you full
Me and you against the world,
burn it over to find our place.
Speak a million words times two
just to hear one word form you
It does not matter what people will say,
when I am with you there is only day
Our existence is not diminished by ignorance
If your light was extinguished today
I would let mine fade.

Kujichgulia /What People Mean (haiku)

people say, be you
when one does, nouns impale skin
oh, their perspective

No Kiss, An Epiphany

It's the things you think about
In the suffocating darkness
Of a youth's summer night.

I am awaking to hugging you no more
You spent the night and crawled in my bed
Just like you'd done since kids.

Your head on my chest just under my chin
My arm trapped under your body
Looking into the lonely nights to come.

Thankful the darkness still covers me
A few more butterflies over lavender seconds
I know who you are and what I am not.

Move my shoulder from under his head
Turn and tiptoe down to younger days
Riding on each other's bikes like mad demons.

Reading books on your moms back porch
Experiments with my chemistry set
Sharing the stars with the telescope we bought.

Selling candy, mowing lawns, and washing cars
We're thirteen and the past is a sad song's lyrics
Tear at your soul while looking for the missing pieces.

Farewell to your innocent arms
No awkward misinterpretation of personal moments

Out you go tomorrow's light.

When Brokenness Breaks

I am still alive
Dragged across the river bed
Rocks playing Gillespie across my head
Skin torn back expose secret places of my soul
I was stronger than this, daggers always a miss.

Family always knows the center to touch
Friends grafted in left only a stump
Love to see you choke then drown
Can't seem to keep inverted rainbows down
Psychedelic parade car full of clowns.

Astounded when your skin hardens
The soul nourished on the abnormal
Indignant you're strong as the dandelion
breaking through the concrete
Nina's words massaging down to the white meat.

Fish in the sea you know how I feel
blossoms on the trees
you know how I feel
River running free you know how I feel
Sun in the sky you know how I feel
It's a new dawn, new day, a new life for me.

And I'm feelin' good.

Iya Olorun

Songs echoed down the umbilical cord
She shaped the incasing of my soul
A prophecy of molding this life
Sustained me with the dew of her breast
Table filled with sweet and holy manna
Prepared with African remembrances.

Affirming hope when I found discouragement
Beating back fears feeding on my psyche
Taught me to pray for loved ones, and world pains
Meditations quell anger borne in a false united nation
Lay all my heart's pretenses on her altar
With her I will not be an actor.

Wisdom's precious blue diamonds
Blessed she watches over my sunsets
The Maat at the horizon of my tomorrows
Teachings embedded in the strands of my DNA
Presence here in the nucleus of my blood cells
Creation is spiritual, powerful, and feminine.

Iya is the first god I knew.

I Can Dance Too

I jerk my body and move with the rhythm.
My body bends and twists, but it never breaks.
I can dance to music or I can dance to silence.
I don't just dance baby; I am a dance.
Oh, sure a tree can move a little taste.
They sway back and forth and sometimes
bend until they near' touch the ground.
That only happens when the wind blows.
I don't need the wind to move.
I just stand up and it happens.
I begin to undulate and fly through the air.
Pump, hump, bump body shake, feet beats
I dance until my heart begs for relief,
but my body begs for more.
Yeah, I dance all over the place
with my arms spread to the sun
or clutch tight to my body to keep it from
shattering from all the movement.
The trees, the grasses of the prairie,
and the leaves all need the wind to do their thing.
I don't need anything because I am a dance.
And when you are a dance like me,
nothing else needs to be said.

April Shower

This has not been the kind of day
I wanted it to be.
For it should have been a day just
for you and for me.
It began to rain early this
afternoon and it gave great pain
to know I would not be seeing you.

So, I imagined what it would be like
if you were the earth and I the rain.
Showers I would bring as often as you needed.
Together, rain and earth bringing forth the many trees,
and flowers, oh, this would truly please me.

However, today I must be satisfied with lying in
my bed thinking pleasant thoughts.
No matter how hard I tried
mother nature just could not be bought.
Thus, I must wait for another day
when you and I will not be apart.

defiance

beat down and torn up
worse than a rag doll
the wind tosses me back
and forth like a rollin'
tumble weed with no place
to call home.

frail and tired as hell
I push myself off the ground
dust the dirt out of my shirt
and pants and hold my head up.

i'm still standin.

I found me

i had been
running, running, running,
blindly away from me
scared of the reflection
staring soberly back at me.

Me i see
as i peek
around the corner
with childish curiosity
and hesitation.
i have had a sad life sitting by myself.

A rock weighing my soul down.
Drowning in my own tears a night
until one day i had decided to
stop hiding in the shadows of your fears.

The sun came one morning
spread a light so completely
there i was just me,
chorus for me.
i finally understand
things i have always known.
i first chose to close
the windows to my soul
because the picture
too real for you to deal.

I Thought You Should Know

Did you know I was not quite the boy next door?
Often times left alone on the playground
Passed over a thousand times
Stuck out in right field, of softball games.

Did you know high school
was a four-year nightmare
Others going to parties
and hanging out on parking lots
Movies, cutting classes, football team
and popularity with the cheerleading squad
A scrawny, geeky, and smart
drowned by out of style clothes
hidden in the shadows of oversized glasses
No one bothered to ask me.

Did you know I once tried suicide?
Death, a perfect answer to a dumb question
a hole in my soul
Living was painful hell
so dying had to be an ascension
I picked up my feet
walked to the lake shore
on a starred black night
Then I caught a glimmer of me
rolling in on a ripple a small wave
I realized a big wave starts out small
and so do we all.

living quietly

Afraid to play with other children
they might learn who I am
Afraid to laugh out loud,
someone might notice me
Afraid to cross the street,
what I need may be on the other side
Afraid to love hard,
getting hurt would be worse
Afraid to listen to the rain
I might hear a soul
Afraid to dance and move my hips
I might feel silly
Afraid to see the sunshine,
rays may hurt my eyes
Afraid to touch or be touched
it may tear down walls
Afraid to speak
someone might trust my words
Afraid to see the nakedness of my body
it is beautiful
Afraid to play in the rain
it may wash away my tears
Afraid to live out loud
it easier doing what others expect
Afraid to be exactly who I am,
It's all there is…

No Waiting

When I look into your face
I become dizzy
warm, intense, heightened feeling.
Resting my head on you
moist touch of your skin
the world is right again.

A soft kiss on the neck,
the closed lids of my eyes.
We hold each other tighter
No now, or waiting to be.
No waiting anxious, nervous fear.

Anticipation of syncopated conversations
and acts meant to drive us to edges end.
Avoid groping desperately for understanding
For I am the word and you are the definition.
There is no need to look, it is here.

Love.

Orlando Taylor

What It Takes to Hold Me

If your intention is honest
This love I have for you is a melody
deep inside a space known as me
Our piano keys work together
harmony that steadies storms in my mind
Lost my way and faith was not my friend
so be honest about what you need
Speak truth to me at all times
use your hands and heal wounds to my ego
But if this is too much walk away
games played backfire and explode.

My Story

Born to a family of 6 boys and 3 girls
Mu-dear struggling to raise us
strict, you would've thought we were
Jehovah's witness' or a Pentecostal family
No staying up late on a school night
On the front porch by eight and in the house by nine
Known to wake you up with a razor-sharp belt
If you forgot to put the metal trash cans out.

Scrapping, fighting, and biting to get by
Poverty evident by vacant lots, broken bottles,
houses in desperate need of repairs
sharing everything with my brothers even underwear
Five of us in one room, two or three in the same bed
Lord knows I was glad when we got us bunk beds
Stomach always that full, clothes was always clean
Walking over vacant lots heading for school.

Always had someone there to play or be with,
Older sis looking out so my mother could work
lil' girl's trying hard to be grown
Tony is gone, but he was a fly ass brother,
Bobby, called slow, always listening to his radio,
surprise you with the wise words from a childlike mind
Earl, the first of us to go away to school,
achieve what some thought impossible
Keith, was fast and quick on the court
we grew up fighting like cats and dogs,
the truest, intelligent brothers in 'hood that I know

Orlando Taylor

Peanut, always able to crack a joke
turn life's bullshit into flowers and sun beams .

thank God he gave us a jester
to keep poverty from festering
Number eight child, the youngest boy me
Quicker to read than make friends
comfortable with pencil and paper creating
heavens guide and to your star
Number nine at the end of this engine,
the queen, full of strength
and courage, and attitude
critical eye but, yet compassion is her rule.

My father made me an official a ghetto bastard
Alone in understand myself
what matters in this play called life
I couldn't converse and explain my trials
Of a young black man in America,
One day sick in the hospital bed,
doctors said my future was dead
mother's head bowed, in her hands
you were sought, but you never showed up
Thankful for the spirit of a powerful
black mother and stopped looking for a father
in a man who couldn't bother.

In Love

For you I would pull back the heavens
we could see into the fifth dimension.

Astral project your soul
to the four corners of the world
witness all the earth's beauty at once,
much better than an ex-rush.

Crack the earth to its deepest core
warmth through the coldest winters if you need.
Bring you water from the river Nile to quench
your thirst from a long diaspora journey.

Wade into the river's currents, cleansing one another
in the ripples of purity's flow.
Under a grove of trees peacefully
the birds singing their part in life's symphony.

Playfully send a note to you in a bottle,
Unable to verbally express the
emotions locked in my chest
desperate to swallow.

If the stars run like tears
strength from the ancestors I ask
return them to the original dark sea,
saving one to keep for you and me.

CHAPTER TWO

AKOBEN

war ... (within and without)

Uptown-Downtown

'I'm going away for the winter,
South America or Morocco.'
Places where you play bridge
and shuffle board all day.

I'm just gonna try to stay warm this winter.
Put some plastic over the windows
and pray the pipes don't freeze.
If I have some time between jobs
I'll play a few hands of bid.

For dinner tonight let's have steaks
with au gratin potatoes, broccoli and
white wine sauce and French rolls.
Cheese cake with fresh strawberries dessert
thaw the steaks in the microwave.

I made a big pot of beans last night
before laying in my sinking bed.
Big pan of cornbread,
some hot dogs and that's dinner.

Oh, the kids need some new tennis shoes.
Bradley, Jr. can't seem to keep them
a month before he needs a new pair.
Little Man will wear same
clothes this school year as last.

I tried to save some money,
but it just didn't work out.

I'll put patches on the holes
and he'll be fine, I hope.

Orlando Taylor

Oppression

Sun sho' is hot today
Been like dis err day dis week
I don't know what to do
all my fans are goin'
dey might as well be off
'stead of wastin' 'lectricity.

Lawd knows I ain't got
no money for high bills
I wish He make up His min'
and tell the sun to stop shining so hard
Dees chil'ren have to have col' water
an' col' air else dey fall out.

I's just don't know which is worse anymo',
de heat on my back
or de white folks foots on my neck.

Why You Skerred

Why you skerred...

To walk down the street alongside dark meat
I didn't come with a posse to your continent
roundup people in herds,
packed in a wooden stomach
only to be thrown up months later on
the shores of an unknown land
leather whips, metal chains, and other abuse
squeezed language, heritage, and culture
out through their bowels
leaving fresh lumpy clay
perfectly molded for slavery.

Why you skerred of me...
I ate the hot and spicy Jim Crow steaks
changed seats cross over the line
made by the Missouri Compromise
desperately trying to gain knowledge
and wisdom in broken down schools
trying to walk upright, but not too bold
those who dared tasted the bittersweet
burning of Black roses, hanging ornaments,
dripping potent red nectar from their petals
unhealed wounds etched with a craftsman's skill
in my soul like cut stained glass in church
a terrible gift passed to me from ancestors
community with only a survivalist mentality
under the American flag set apart and tied.

Orlando Taylor

Why you skerred of me ...
living in the slums of the penitentiary
continuously beaten by police always innocent
even when their evil deeds are caught on TV
young brothers with no dreams beyond eighteen
public schools are inadequate,
constantly balancing on bankrupt
cry to politicians like beggars clanging change in a cup
ghettos, projects, and urban blight
kindling on the fire of insurrection.

So, why you skerred,
How many times have I been president

Black Today and Tomorrow
(if you are ashamed)

Hankty folk, that's all they is.
Thinkin' they're better than other people
they got cars, houses and a little money.
Running from the city to the suburban
refuge in the middle of the night
'cause they know white folks don't want 'em there.
Never to be heard from again in the ghetto,
except of course, at some social
gathering to help "economically deprived"
children and the "endangered species."

You have nerve to look at me
down the sides of your broad nose
'cause I don't wear Nautica, Tommy Hilfiger, Liz Claiborne.
I'm fine with my Old Navy specials and the J. C. Penny Outlet.
I'm mo' concerned with the label on my soul
than a name on my clothes.

For some of y'all my color is too Black.
My nose too fat, and the contour of my lips
just a little too thick.
A butt as big as a sunny day
and dance like a Betsy bug on hot griddle.
Oh, excuse me you so fine and refined now.
Grits and co'nbread not enough fo' you
No more fatback, neck bones, 'coon, pinto beans,
and fried chicken.

It's split pea soup, Caesar salads, veal,

leg of lamb, a rare steak, Brussels sprouts,
and a small wedge of cheesecake no sweet potato pie.

But hold up, wait a minute, look what's going on.
Black is in again and look who's back.
Kente cloth is hotter than yo' mama was
the night you were conceived.
Locks like you some Rasta man
ain't nevah been to the Caribbean
barely point out Africa on a world map.
Hair is cut short to show the kinky-curl of yo' Black world.
Ain't we bad? Ain't we funky now? Ain't we Black as can be?
Ummm…mmmm.
Yes, I still relax my hair and
I don't wear clothes made in Nigeria.
But, if I did, I would be truer than you.
What you do not understand is this:
being African is not a learned art
it is what you are in the DNA.

Black Rage

Still sitting at the kitchen table
Is it ok to come into the living room
Three fifths a human evident
in almost every statistic.

Underpaid, under employed
Under educated, marginalized
to the shadows of American society
And the concrete of choking ghettos.

Education, assimilation, integration
An insidious conspiracy to brainwash African children
Bash their head on rocks of expectations
A stream of unfulfilled dreams leak from their minds.

You ask why you are all so angry, why so mad?
Hung from trees like your clothes we washed
Beatings a reminder we are not owners just visitors
Watching through a kaleidoscope of American promises.

Looked at with disdain and disgust
For the poison you bussed the world over
We did nothing but exist
Show me the treaty we signed on for this parade.

Tired of surviving on the leftovers of white privilege
Subsistence not a lesson in existentialism
Tired of bandaging the welts on my people's souls
We suffer from a collective mental psychosis.

Watching black families over generations
Anesthetized into thinking that this life is living
While window shopping on white lives
Dancing sugar plums muffles our screams.

Why are you angry? You are lucky to be here.
We've earned the right to be here
Changed our names to a discarded harvest
We couldn't change the melanin.

Folks From de Souf

I woke early wid my min' stay'd on Jesus
I woke early with my min' stay'd on Jesus.

They packed up dat boy and all his belongin's
rushed him outta town.
White men say he know'd betta
than to be lookin' at a white woman.
His fam'ly ain't heard f 'om dat chile since.

Lawd, Lawd, Lawd, help me on dis journey.
Oh, help me on dis here journey.

They cut down dat tree et de crossroads
Can't say I'm sad to see hit go neether
Ooo wee, hit bring back some awful mem'ries
of dat day dey hung James Earl on dat tree
Lawd hit was a fritful sight to see
White women and men screamin',
an' us a cryin' and prayin'. Didn't do no good tho'
I told dat boy don' go talkin' 'bout
rights an votin' an such
where white folks could heayah.
Heard 'em sayin',
"Uppity nigra we'll show yous
the most important right you got
de right to die. String 'im up!"

I woke early wid my min' stay'd on Jesus .
I woke early with my min' stay'd on Jesus.
Packed up all my things, my wife,

47

my chil'ren, and my hopes.
Heading fo' a betta life, a new job
and a place I came home.
Goin' norf to New York
I hit de city and fell straight
to my knees on de concrete.
Thank you, Lawd, for deliverin' me
I feel free fo' the firs' time in my life.
Thank you, Jesus.

Police officer tapped me firmly on my shoulder
"Boy, git up off your knees blockin' the sidewalk
For all dees good white people
I bet you here from straight f 'om the south.
Well, we don' wontcha up heayah either
to the ghetto is where you's betta go!"

How I made it ovah, how did I make it ovah.
You know my soul look back an' wonda
how did I make ovah.
Somebody show when He's been on time.

Woman

A slave named woman…
gave birth to all the masses of this earth
uterus tearing, as she bears one ungrateful soul
Raising them into powerful races and nations,
traveling the lands claiming everything in sight,
no incense, gold, and wealth but she is free to beg
the unworthy female is responsible for all.

Raised, herded, sold, transported across
the continents and seas as cattle in the bottom
of rusty barrels sold in packaged marriages
"Would you like paper or plastic, sir"
with that new slave/bride.

Equal to nothing, a fourth-class citizen
a beast of burden, deemed useful to men
all the abuse and abasement directed at you
Even enemies get aid and loans to rebuild
but for the first god known to men
awaits desecration and ashes.

Much is demanded, expected
mold children into men and woman of strength
bear the weight from those who take your love
inject drops of life into your soul
giving up the fruit of your uterus without a scream
holding on to your desires and dreams
no one knows, and no one is listening.

A slave named woman
pledge to restore the fallen stones
scattered about your temple in confusion
co-pharaoh of this world and universe
make men gaze and weep over your beauty
remembering, mother-woman
the first god known to all children.

Black National Anthem

My country 'tis not for me.
Sweet land of liberty?
Of thee I still cannot sing.

Land where thousands of my fathers died
leaving no room for any pilgrim's pride.
Kidnapped in broad daylight
Open sores ring my neck
crisscrossing scars on my back
document the chaotic American dream
cross the southern Compromise
beaten with a book
to break the segregation threshold
From every mountainside
freedom is ringing
but 'tis not for me.

Of thee I still cannot sing.

shit is all you get for dinner

shit is all you get for dinner
that's what you told me yesterday

my feet hurt from all the marching i've been doing
where your dogs bit me i used alcohol to disinfect
my neck is sore from ropes
hang me from American trees
smell of my burning flesh intoxicates me
i'm tired of sitting in praying in
begging in and protesting
i want to come home
i'm hungry may i have something to eat

shit is all you get for dinner
i thought i might have something different today

i asked for a job
but you won't let me run anything
i'm in many public offices
but the oval office is off limits
overcrowded the jails
where's always room on the streets i'm hungry
i want something to eat
shit is all you get for dinner
i told you twice before that i was hungry!
i'm bustin' down the door
dumpin' caps with my .44
in the ass of the first muthafucka
standing between me and the dinner table
i'm not gonna be hungry no more

A Word from Little Black Boys to America

Dear America,
I've had something on my mind
for quite some time now

I may be a bastard child
because my father did not stay
Still I grow strong and intelligent
under the love and care of my mother
many of us have fathers
we consider as our best friends
But even if neither of my parents loved me
Olu does and He has never made a mistake

Media constantly talks about me
Defined by my worst elements
other groups defined by their best.
Labeled "learning disorder," "behavioral disorder,"
and "at-risk youth"
destined to end up in jail, or in a grave
a hopeless burden or parasite on society.

Statistics say 25% of Black men 17-24
years of age are in jail or under court supervision.
Fine, but what's happenin'
with the other 75% of us?
Going to school and getting degrees,
ask Clark, Xavier, Howard, and Tuskegee.
We go to work everyday supporting ourselves
and maybe a family.
We are inventors, entrepreneurs,

construction workers, businessmen,
laborers and doctors.
you might get buried by the dust.
we kicking up from our legacy.

Not all A's on my report card of life
you neither so stop writing, studying,
and theorizing about what you think
And make changes to fix your mess.

Christmas...What it is?

The hustle and bustle begin
the day after Thanksgiving in the malls
with the ringing of the cash registers
Jaie gets a truck, Shontelle a Black Barbie doll,
and DeAndre some new urban attire.

All the money is spent and
credit is pushed to the limit
A sumptuous dinner is prepared
on the stove with a prayer
gas company won't mind
the payment being late this month.

I can't help but wonder what a cold day
long ago as a caravan from the east
followed a star in search of a child has
to do with a red suit, white beard
and black patent leather boots?

Hip-hop

Momma shouted,
"Would you turn that music as you call it down boy!"
"Why you dis'n my music Momma?"
" 'Cause it ain't nuthin
but bad language and jungle rhythms.
That's why it's so many juvenile delinquents now.
Hippity hop junk!
Play some real music!"

Hip-hop is real music,
Momma and so much more, baby.
The bad language?
Yeah, it's bad sometimes.
But, so are the feelings they express.
Bad like the cops harassing
me 'cause I wear a baseball cap
and a hoody when I'm on the streets.
Bad like so many my sisters
and brothers dying of AIDS.
Bad 'cause I can't understand
why Black people been here since befo' Columbus
and still can't get jobs like the white folks.
Yeah, we going to college,
but ain't like thousands of us livin' large
Yeah, it's b-a-d language,
but so is the sit-u-a-tion.

The beats bump loud throughout the streets.
not louder than the baby cryin' in the bed
it's been all day since she's been fed.

My Scars Are My Birthmark

Not louder than the sirens
in the streets of the 'hood.

Not louder than the screams of girlfriend
hollin' at her man
Not louder than the 9mm or the A. K. A's
driving by as people duck down
on the ground and kiss this life goodbye.
It's loud but not loud enough
to drown out my pops whuppin' on me
'cause he so afraid I'm gonna be just like him:
Nothin'.

Funky, pulsing butt naked, booty-type
style beats run wild throughout the streets.
Soothing the outrage within my soul
as I feel the 'hood closin' in on me.
The music is not just wild-wild,
but crazee-wild, angry-wild, sad-wild mellow-wild,
I'mtiredofthesameol', fullafullabullshitwild, kind a beats.
Yeah, jungle beats baby 'cause I live
 e'rday in the concrete jungle.

The words are poison?
Poison brings knowledge and
awareness of what the fuck is happenin' around me
This poison helps me verbalize how I feel,
what I'm thinkin' in this cra-zee place.
I want so bad to be on a positive tip.
Yet when I look out my window
I'm reminded in livin' color
that "positive" is not where I live.

Orlando Taylor

Free
(for Bethany and other sisters like her)

her hair is cut so short
you can see the skin on her head.
what she trying to prove?

nothing.
that's the point.
my womanhood is not defined by the length of my hair.
i'm not wearing some carbon copy hairstyle
out of some Black girl magazine.
i'm being me, and not shay, latitia, tonya, shaunshare
or moniqueka.
free, that's me.

she talks so loud to people,
like she tryin' to be seen.

No, i'm not.
you just can't pigeonhole me
into some small-minded idea of femininity.
you know that meek, quiet, unassuming,
sit on a pedestal look pretty, be a good girl,
stay at home, support your man
do what i tell you to bullshit ass description.
i speak my mind.
i tell how i feel when i feel it.
you can hold me; you can touch me.
But i'm a woman with all its positive connotations.

Look gal, act like a woman.

that's just it, don't act like a woman,
be a woman.

there are already too many wanna-be's
perpetrating womanhood but actin' mo' like ho's
o-kay, o-kay check this out.
i'm in school i don't have any my baby daddies,
i do the club scene, but no trickin' with
every demarco, antoine, raymando, shwaun, tom
and let us not forget dick.
meanwhile try closin' yo' legs and
open up that thing between your shoulders.
elevate yo'self and stop this
ridiculous hoochie-mama parade.

but, i'm just being me, free!

Orlando Taylor

Drug Dealer Bullshit

There you are, holding your
manhood in your hands.
Pants so low the back pockets
fall to your knees a thug fo' sho',
standin' on a street corner
staring down folks with the hardest face
practiced hours in mirror at mamma's place.
hand to hand illegal transactions
pursuing the American nightmare
money, power, and sex.
No consideration for the precipitation of
European thinking bring to our people:
take whatever and leave nothing.

System is raping you of your freedom
But they caught you with five rocks,
possession is a bitch.
Hasn't dawned on you how each night
You ripped the innocence
from your own community as she screamed
"please babee, please",
with a jack-o-lantern grin you
push her on her back and forced your
injection, erection deep into her skin
again and again releasing a potent euphoric
cream she can never get out of her dreams.

You know me
I sold my ass all day long
Niggas bang the walls of my uterus
Until it was, bloody, bruised, and useless

all my tithes and offerings to my god
so, he would bless me
with a trip to seventh heaven
Desecrated temple had dried like
A dying dandelion in a field
I gave my 10-year-old baby girl
To those who weren't afraid to
And I drowned out her melodic
screams with a metal dick.

You know me
brother family hate to see
things always leave the house with me.
scared of what I do to get what I need.
Did many dirty, pulled a gun on my brother
Had to get that paper somehow.
My body is a wasteland,
play a funeral dirge on my bony mal-fed ribs.
I die to my self-dignity
Washing ballas' cars for half a rock.
Rent what's left of my car
to young cats who ain't got no license.
In dark alleys everything is fo' sale.

I know you thinking me
"you don't know me, What I been through.
I'm just out here trying to survive!"
A fence you constantly jump in defense,
Running from responsibility.
Using the harshness of life to justify
Thinkin' your over exaggerated machoism
makes you more man than me.
In reality you weak,

not able to deal with sacrifice
Or struggle in the spirit of our elders.

Though you keep running, running, running
you're still standing still
in shit that only men can create.
Running, running, running
afraid to look truthfully
at cracked fragmented images of self.
Running, running, running
From the true Black man
Running, running, running
Shouting where my niggas at?
they cart you off to the penitentiary
crying you really are not man enough
For you were a gatekeeper
to the hellish prison for your own people.
One day I can shout,
"Where my bruthas at..."
and there won't be silence.

Poverty

made me strong survive many storms
taught me not to give up keep moving
encouraged me to set goals
others said they were unattainable

gave me the blessings of a meal prepared
no matter that it seemed spare
created horrific images of desperate men
the acts they do to claim manhood

taught me how to improvise
two-square drawn on the asphalt
football on glass and rock filled lots
alley the track and field near me
hold a dime until it hollered dollar
brought me close to family
in good and bad times

gave me dreams of a life with meaning
despite the nightmares I saw around me
knocked me down stole the inhale of my breath
strengthened the deepest crevices of my soul

Poverty is neither friend nor enemy
but a permanent part of my journey
like a coat wrapped around me

Unholy War
(Trump's war with Iran)

Sisters don't let your men fight in this unholy war
Don't let them die for him
Most ungodly man to ever lead this land
He ain't worth their blood's gold
Sisters don't let your men fight in this unholy war.

They love this fighting shit
been here too many times after war
still have you walking through the back door
Don't more damaged black families
Let alone my sisters deep blue scorched soul.

Sisters don't let your men fight in this unholy war
Don't let them die for him
Most ungodly man to ever lead this land
He ain't worth their blood's gold
Sisters don't let your men fight in this unholy war.

America never killed anyone to keep me free
Food on the table and beautiful
white picket fences nuclear family
Hey, middle class we poppin' over herr
Our blood and bones seeping into soil
Inner child's veins all clogged with Jim Crow
Redlining us into wholes
Sundown towns to keep us at bay
Lynching galore and the utter destruction
of all the black towns calloused souls build
Even the white house
Sisters don't let your men fight in this unholy war

My Scars Are My Birthmark

Don't let them die for him
Most ungodly man to ever lead this land
He ain't worth their blood's gold
Sisters don't let your men fight in this unholy war.

Do whatever it's yours to decide
Get reparations in writing before you go
they'll throw your ass in jail for trying to steal
I'm just trying to get you to understand
what their asking you to fight for
Is not in any way worth them fighting for.

Sisters don't let your men fight in this unholy war
Don't let them die for him
Most ungodly man to ever lead this land
He ain't worth their blood's gold
Sisters don't let your men fight in this unholy war.

Without Sanctuary

They took an African woman and put her in a cage
Left on display for more than a hundred days
White children laughed at her threw
food and rocks in her face
This thing too different to be human
But she was, belonging to the original
The first black woman strippin' for her freedom.

Screaming ancestors running for life
Trying to get away from the demon catchers
caught his scream a blues song
ain't it sad this day he says
Keep running 'til you get to the stream
My death is a song, follow the northern star
So, keep running away, running away,
Running away, running away,
Don't worry 'bout me, I'll die, you fly.

An echo to the bodies hanging from trees
Onlookers take pictures with families
Body writhing and contorted, dead
Once beautiful skin the color of the universe
Now burned to the palest of ashes
Layers of brokenness unscathed by the fire
Oh lawd, Oh lawd, Oh lawd
Let me down
Oh lawd, Oh lawd, Oh lawd
Let me down.

Filling African men with shame

Because they couldn't protect their kin
Digging their fingers into one's skin
Silent howls at an unconcerned moon
Begging Oshun to dig the pain out with a spoon.

Oh lawd, Oh lawd, Oh lawd Oh lawd,

Connected by blood, shame, blame
Anger, fear and inability to exact vengeance
Pressed together with the force of an ocean
These are the bonds we share in America
a place where I have no sanctuary?

Orlando Taylor

A Prayer to Oya

Woke to text from my older brother
Like the night that I lost my mother
White folks finally destroy the Northside
All the lost history of black lives
My old neighborhood in the Ville is dirt roads
Feeling like I'm three hundred years old.

I spoke to god last night
Please hit my enemies with all of your might
She said "baby don't you worry I got all this"
How, when all I see is a bunch of shit?
I spoke to god last night
Can you help me my people they assed out?
None of this hate makes any sense
I spoke to god last night.

They dragged us from your bosom to the Eastside
Millions died in the ocean trying to get right
Sisters had their wombs cut open for their pride
They whipped the roads home on my brothers back
I got six African groups inside me
Tell me how this situation came to be.

Rape was a big in the southeast
Spoke too strong they cut off your meat
Hung on trees like ornaments
That's why we dump our soul into music
They're near the end and they can't quit
Tell me mama Oya what's the meaning of it

My Scars Are My Birthmark

We've been waiting on your love for a minute
She'll be coming round Sirius B
when she comes Hurry up
She'll be coming round Sirius B
when she comes Hurry up
She'll be comin', she'll be comin',
she'll be comin' she'll be comin',
It thought you loved us, what the fuck!

I spoke to god last night
Please hit my enemies with all of your might
Don't you worry I got this
How, when all I see is a bunch of shit?
I spoke to god last night
Can you help my people they assed out?
None this hate makes any sense
Your people dying because of it
I spoke to god last night.

She didn't listen.

Tragic Magic

I've been black since '67
455, 520 hours and still counting
it's not just about me
Got caught up with what brothers should
or should not be
Battles that need to be fought
Words that need to be passionately
and intellectually delivered
With all the righteousness that any
good black man has
But the collective euphoric anger
induced psychosis security blanket we carry
when our manly bodies are not enough.

Black melanin is power
reflects the universe
Symbol that you are her's first
Before the sun kissed your skin
The original false curse
you struggle not to believe in
Cracked mirrors of self-perception
Black male manhood's affirmation
Forget you sometimes sit on the floor
with your knees to your chin
holding back a soul eruption
like tectonic plates crashing into
one another at 3000 miles and running
Leaving only a silent sonic psychedelic
black light poster scream.
Every black man would be ashamed to meme

Living in that tragic overwhelms
the magic a spell that sustains.

I found me

i had been
running, running, running,
blindly away from me
scared of the reflection
staring soberly back.

Me i see as i peek
around the corner
with childish curiosity
and hesitation.

i have had a sad life sitting by myself.
A rock, not of my choice weighing down my soul.
Drowning in my own tears many a night
until one day i had decided to
stop hiding behind the trees of fears.

The sun came one morning
spread a light so completely
there i was just me
it sang a chorus for me.
I finally understand
things i have always known.
i first chose to close the windows
to my soul because the picture
too real for me to deal.

Educational Capitalism (sijo)

Survival of the fittest will turn our schools into jungles

Manufactured people with tailored brains primed for corporate needs

Educating our children is paramount, remove greed

Orlando Taylor

The Passion of Nat Turner

I

A young Afrikan enslaved as stud chattel
Saw the torment of life on the plantation
Wanted to kill the white man in battle
Ancestors' vision's filled prophet with passion.

He meditated and prepared in wilderness
Mother wondered is he Moses-o, my Nat Turner
He was not remorseful about Father's business
A voice like a trumpet's bray, the great exhorter.

Aloof from most of his kin, not one to prate
As an acolyte, even adults asked for guidance
Stars, nightly comfort, had to ask to see his mate
The present must not lead to lifelong permanence.

No rest, know patience, until time is pregnant
They will not repent, but work to keep us stagnant.

II

Time dilated to the needed centimeters
Militia formed like the Angel of Death's coming
The first to expire was Nat's personal jailers
God's wrath for enslavement of the hue-man being.

Band of male spirits determined armed for revolt
Penitentiaries of death fell in Southampton
Filled with power of righteousness and a rifles bolt

My Scars Are My Birthmark

Showing common courage to start an insurrection.

The battle of ages came to an abrupt end
Pharisees begged they sacrifice of the black lamb
Savior hanged and skinned, proof crackers do not pretend
He broke the legacy yoked on us by Uncle Sam.

We are awed by your courage and sing your praise
Katrina uncovered the same apartheid malaise.

Push Through
(Inspired by Talib Kweli's - Push Thru)

Three of my siblings gone
Spirits now wandering
What you gonna do now
Floating through life time to get stable
Makes this reality instead of a fable.

So many watchin' bettin'
I'm gonna amount to nothing
While they shucking, hustling and bustling
Running around in a box dancing in the same spot
Then it hit me an epiphany
I'm a poet writer and a vocalist.

Now time to get up and do something
Bus' and amazing verse
Make earthquakes on this earth
See I'm Cain y'all Abel
You about to witness the R&B murder
Killing you sexy flexy divas
With lyrical flows and treble clef blows.

I rise at daybreak
Clouds hide the sun rays
Quick sand and mistakes
Walls to get through
I fight the good fight
Even on the bad days
It's time to speak my life. I'm gonna push through.

Sankofet for Healing

Grandparents tilled lands, a mosquito's meal for children
Hands diggin' into the earth, their life had worth
Working with the awakening of day, past apex of the sun
Trees' roots exposed, American soil will never nurture
Common seed together produced food for Afrikan nature
Not much money, family ties warded off spiritual poverty
No definition needed, we understood community.

Community desolate like random smiles in a dank bar room
Waters of solution surround like the dusty Sahara by oceans
Mis-educated minds stagnated waiting to be told what to do
Trees' roots exposed, American soil will never nurture
Searching for the Great Black Leader, forgetting the one inside
Elders don't speak to the youth lost in a disrespectful loop
We see through apathetic glasses expecting little of this
generation.

Generation next I sing from the book of Tears and Lamentations
You must eat crumbs thrown from the table of this nation's chaos
Afrika, heal the diaspora dipped in concrete, asphalt and steel
Trees' roots exposed, American soil will never nurture
History, economics, and languages are keys to our dilemma
GOP and its corporate fascists will erase muted middle class
Make reality the actions started by our great grandparents.

Orlando Taylor

CHAPTER THREE
NKONSONKONSON

human relations

A New Banner

Oh I can see the stars.
'Cause Mr. Charlie won't stop
beaten me upside my head
with the banner.

Vinegrove Groove

In the near distance a police car screams in urgency
an ambulance following close behind.

Night
on an unnaturally warm day in May
A cool wind blows across the trees
the weeds that were once grass.
Low music emanates from a neighbor's car,
the "Quiet Storm" moves through the hood
while many lay down to rest.
down the alley dogs bark at a robber.
Just a familiar wino relieving
the day's beverages.

The rain stops
a layer of moisture covers the streets.
Cars move slowly,
Tiny soldiers walk the streets,
Mama and Daddy are too busy
to pay any attention to their children.

A wonderful calmness
settles on the neighborhood.
Fathers return home from work
mothers settle the children into bed
Sounds of the night are pleasant and dangerous.

Orlando Taylor

Livin'

You haven't lived
'til on a hot summer day stripped
to your shorts you play like crazy in
the spray of the water from a fire hydrant.
Errbody screaming 'cause it's so much fun.

You haven't lived
'til you've watched from your window
the sun rising over the tops of ragged houses
Eyes fixed on the orange face
as faint hints of heat fill the spaces in yo' cheeks
For a moment you ponder life's meaning.

You haven't lived
'til you've played to near midnight
hide-n-go-seek, red-light-green-light and dodge ball
Then you get called in for baths and bed
Eager to do it all over again.

You haven't lived
'til you hear endless arguments
between a man and his woman.
Your little eyes watch in horrific wonder
as she soulfully screams for someone
to beat out the engulfing flames
He set her on fire because he needed
mo' money to get high.

You haven't lived
until you feel the small fingers of a child

desperately clutched around your neck
He thought you had left him
but you were only in the next room
Then you have lived.

Orlando Taylor

Thinkin' Bout Leavin'

Have you ever awakened one mo'nin
exactly the same as you did the other
and couldn't figure out what you were s'pose to be doin'?
It clicks in yo' head e'rthing is the same.
Same clothes, same house, same job, same car
same boss, same tired negroes at work
All of 'em complainin' 'bout things
they know they won't try to change.

Then you turn and look at that ol' car
you prayin' gone make it thru the winta
It's lookin' pretty good all of sudden
'cause you wondering how far
it could git you outta this city.
Just leave, never lookin' back
You only listen to the wind whippin'
around your head.

I wanna go someplace
where no one knows my name
To have no past, no future
just the here and now
I won't have to live up to
the expectations of others
Accept me as I am or leave me alone
One day baby... one day.

Let me put my socks and shoes on,
'cause people look at you crazy
if you one minut' late for work

Inside Blue

I

weighted by the day
i sat down on the curb
as i watched the sun go down i grew sad
prayed all day
but was not heard
i jumped on the wind
ran to the place where sun meets the earth
put my hands up under the light
hard as i tried i could not keep
the sun from going down
heavens laughed at my desperation
but i cried when my soul died.

II

thunder from a summer storm
awakened me from a restless night of sleep
slowly i swung my legs
and sat up on the edge of the bed
lightning pierced the night
my eyes closed violently
the rain drummed against the window
i walked over and looked out
rain ran like rivers in the streets
i wondered if it would make things
new or a reminder of how blue i am.

III

the sun died a year ago the days are long
cold sleepless
i find myself up late
sitting in the dark
in the middle of the living room floor
saying hello to many hours beyond
midnight my life is a journey down
a dark alley there is no light
i hear no movement
save the thudding footfall of my own steps
i am waiting dying
to step out into the warm reign of sun
at the end of the alley.

How can we

How can we be free?
for when you say God Bless America it's not inclusive
are you inviting me to come in and kick off my shoes?
last time I looked up, I got beat with the banner
saw stars but, don't know if they was spangled
Langston said bebop started in this manner.

How can we honestly live free?
if I am accosted and harassed while driving black
In every major case I am a suspect, a black man
in a skull cap, you know the sketch
leave my wallet at home to avoid forty shots.

How can we be free?
the jails are bursting, full with a precious birth
most locked down resemble me
Where is the line for the jury selection,
presiding over America's crimes?
The charges are kidnapping, attempted genocide,
and breaking and entry on African land.

How can we be free?
Materialism is another player strangling our needs
Ain't hatin' on the rich, 'cause my people
like to shine naturally everyday
diamonds like pieces of the sun shining from our ears
the planets wrapped in links around our wrists
the power of sun or the moon hanging from your neck
shining like the rest of Olu's elements.

Time to use this strength for our survival
More important than any gems twinkling.

a sto'm

a sto'm is a comin'
i smell the rain
hear its presence in the silence
ants have stopped working
birds have stilled songs
children stopped giddy laughter
oh my, a sto'm is sho' nuf a'comin
and it's gonna rain.

let it rain, oh all over me
cover me and quiet my soul's
low song if only for a moment,
drops of water dance upon my skeen
cleanse me betta
than the jordan that naaman bathed in
wash over me and drown my pain
like a fifth of bourbon does my personal issues
waitin' on this heyah sto'm a long time
a dope fiend without fo' a day
knows how i feel.

We all fucked up

World governments are coming down
Can't turn on the tele without pictures
Somebody getting their head blown off
Corporate thieves destroying millions
Just to pocket a few dollars
Politicians stealing leaving people with pennies
We all fucked up.

Breaking what the angels handed down
Throwing away our chance to live beyond the stars
Sell yourself to be popular on social media
Children's future sold for fossil fuel
But folks worried about what I'm doing?
We all fucked up.

Women used as incubators for men's seed
Clitoris mutilated numb she is controlled
Stoned to death for being a victim of rape
Nose chopped off if she disobeyed
A whore for living life on her own terms
foundation of mankind unappreciated
We all fucked up.

Breaking what the angels handed down
Throwing away our chance to live beyond the stars
Sell yourself to be popular on social media
Children future sold for fossil fuel
But folks worried about what I'm doing?
We all fucked up.

Children often used by adult men
Schools create zombies not great ideas
Suicide, adult predilections no respect
Future is esoteric few feel there is one
fifteen minutes under someone else's sun
We all fucked up.

Breaking what the angels handed down
Throwing away our chance to live beyond the stars
Sell yourself to be most popular on social media
Children sold for fossil fuel
But folks worried about what I'm doing?
We all fucked up.

War not enough let the planet supernova
Resources paid by the low vibration of souls
Ethnic revenge while barons swoop in
Colonization and racist exploitation linger
In the end the human spirit been poisoned
Humanity will find its end
We all fucked up.

Breaking what the angels handed down
Throwing away our chance to live beyond the stars
Sell yourself to be popular on social media
Children future sold for fossil fuel
Trans-gendered, Same-gendered, bi-sexual
The mess that exists we didn't create
But folks worried about what I'm doing?
We all fucked up

Where yo' god

Praying on knees twenty-four-seven
to get whiff of heaven
Dylan Roof blew up the house
just give you proof
I thought you was gangsta
now what you gonna do?

Where yo' god at?

First god I knew was little black woman
Holdin' it down with a pearl handled .45
My protector never failed to feed me
Couldn't afford the best never naked in the streets
Kissed my wounds made them feel healed instantly
Never starved a day in my life that's my light.

Where yo' god at?

In slavery holding a string called maybe
Beat with whip and the book 'til you pray
Sky daddy come an' whisk away
Three-fifths of see that's Christian
Hung from a tree swinging southern breezes.

Pop-pop goes the guns before you put your hands up
Mother's bitter tears fall scorch the ground
Heavy with, dear mother, can you save me?
Where yo' god at?

Two years old death visited my sleeping crib

two large rats ready to gnaw me into the afterlife
She destroyed them snatched me to her bosom
Screaming supplications to the black Madonna
Heavy with life, dear mother god, can you save me?

Where yo' god at?

First god I ever knew was little black woman
Holdin' it down with a chrome .45 with pearl handle
My protector and she never failed to feed me
Couldn't afford the best walked not naked in the streets
Kissed my wounds made them feel healed instantly
Never starved a day in my life now that's my light.

Where yo' god at?

First god I knew was little black woman
Holdin' it down with a pearl handled .45
My protector never failed to feed me
Couldn't afford the best never naked in the streets
Kissed my wounds made them feel healed instantly
Never starved a day in my life that's my light.

I'm still waiting, to see, where yo' god at?

Orlando Taylor

Haven't Lived This Life

Dragged from our homes on Africa's warm shores
Iron chain premonition of the life to come
Some chose a watery grave given to ocean predators
The belly of a wooden barrel, shared excrement
Sardine experience, alive but dazed the whole way
Too few rebel, return to the bosom of our origin
Sunlight doesn't cleanse scars from the slave trader's hand.

Traded with the same aplomb they have for cattle
Studded to make the strongest mayors and bucks
Black, soulless, and ugly as hell, a lie
Couldn't stay away from black quarters
raping 'til your twisted pleasure filled
Black babies cut from wombs consumed given fear
Thrown to gators as bait your pain does not equate
Hamite justification, lawd can't save the southerner.

One rung below the worst white person
perverted Jesus bible parable
Scraps thrown to us cause like its trash
We called it soul now you desperate to taste
But you ain't lived this life
You just responsible for it.

Surviving and building no phrenology
Clawed Jim Crow burned and with a fiery cross
Black Wall Streets scorched by envy
We rise again you afraid of truth: we are gods
At times lost in a malaise of racism and brutality
Still hear the whispers of Africa's beckoning

My Scars Are My Birthmark

One rung below the worst white person
perverted Jesus bible parable
Scraps thrown to us cause like its trash
We called it soul now you desperate to taste
But you ain't lived this life
You just responsible for it.

Marching through streets with Martin
Third eye wants to burn it down with Malcolm
Dogs chewing on our bodies like rag dolls
Water breaking skin we offer a defiant grin
Black people still this nation's juiciest fruit
Die shouting our rage now's the time for living
Black power fist to this perverse system.

We still being riddled with bullet holes
A whole city drowned the nation didn't blink
Police use military grade force
Putting a fist to freedom's teeth
Black Lives Matter hands up guard down
They trying to erase us from existence
Turn towards Africa your continence
Deep tissue mental damage Africans still standing.

We gone have real freedom soon
tear down the tyranny of this system
Make them wish their ancestors
had never landed on an African bay

Soul Brother #1: Tony the Tiger

(in memory of Anthony Taylor ~ born in
the 50's)

To be home by dinner was hard
on a young blood trying to learn the streets
Carrying a switchblade and dreamed of a zip gun.
Dressed in window pane jeans, silk butterfly collar shirt,
and a pair of leather platform shoes.
Apple hat on top and handkerchief around the neck
Real fly in a leisure suit, white shirt opened just right.

Takin' pride in showing his younger brothers
around the neighborhood.
Kickin' them out some change
and showing them the newest handshakes.
Make sure his brothers were some kool, Black cats.
'Cause "Black is beautiful" and "take ten"
was the battle cry.

He had a traveling soul growing cold
stuck in an oppressive city moving like cooling lava.
Satchel over his shoulder or a pouch on his side.
Gave gifts from his heart to us it was priceless,
he thought of other people all the time.

You could hear the Stylistics with one step and
Robert Flack with the fall of the next.
As he swayed to the left Marvin Gaye cried,
Mercy, mercy me, things ain't what the used to be.
To the right, Donny Hathaway's, for all we know
this may only be a dream.

MY SCARS ARE MY BIRTHMARK

This is how I felt the night I got the call
Your spirit had been taken from me.

A painful life for my "Tony Bolognie" to live.
He began to check out gradually.
Hanging with scandalous "friends"
Gave a damn about bipolar condition.
As long as he had some money errthang was kool.
Let the money run out and so did they.
He found a new friend got real tight quick.
It was a fire and he loved to get it under his skin.

Gotta, Gotta take me hi-yah...
Gotta, Gotta take me hi-yah...

He and his friend hung out 'til the end.
On the corner near Kossuth and Grand
trying to buy fuel fo' his fire
Robbed him and put five rockets in his body.
One... two...
he fell back and off went one of his shoes.
Three... four...
he won't be able to buy his fire no more
Five, is all the way live, baby
Five plus one, is the Taylors
him and his brothers.
Give me five on the back-hand side
The number of brothers left behind
Now I understand all too well
when I see my brother's picture:
Marvin's verse, movin' down the line ...

I hate you

I
(to the other tony)

you were there when five shots
burned a path to his vital organs.
the night his spirit was freed
you knocked on my mother's door
and ran to your car,
yelled back from the street
Tony's in the hospital,
shrank to coward's position under a rock.

a poor man's funeral was all we could afford.
just us his coffin at a military cemetery.
there was sun, no more son.
surprise, there was no you.
shame and guilt are heavy burdens
weighing on your dark spirit.
i have no sympathy for you until you are ready
to tell us the truth about february 16, 1998.
a reoccurring memory badly scratched vinyl.
may nights haunt the cracks of your selfish mind.
your dreams filled with his tears and screams.
i thought you should know how much i hate you.

II
(to liberals)

certain white folks will smile in yo' face

and hate you behind your back
smile in yo' face and speak words of corruption
cause destruction tearing your spirit apart
smile in your face
and plant mine fields of obstacles in the way of life,
liberty, and the pursuit of happiness
smile in yo' face
incredibly offended when you speak
with knowledge and authority
showing you are capable and think
and even reason on your own
first to clutch purse
and call police oh,
don't you know
i hate you?

III
(father)

a father whose figure i've been told i reflect
possess, except your presence.
i grew strong with no you.
you assuming no responsibility.
when i was a score and one,
i reached out for you.
there could be a father in you
or maybe just a little guidance
in the end, i guess that's
all there was, an end.
I want you know
i hate you.

ghetto roses

Struggling for survival in a place
she is not supposed to be.
Trying desperately to make a way
against the odds.
Withstanding the burdens of life
the scorching heat of the sun heavy on her neck.
She's there daily without much complaint.

Washing, cleaning, working
not much time for anything personal.
Working as a cook here, a waitress over
there beating the system, a little just to make
meat to feed seven.
Pushing through the rough
soil like a dandelion.

Working hard in the kitchen
Arms burned cooking with a bad stove.
Hands feel like sandpaper sewing patches
more than once on old clothes.
Voice sometimes strained from
yelling at motley little boys.
Back strong but spirit weary drifting
with the remains of the day.
She will be there tomorrow
strong like a dandelion.

Sweating and singing with the music
the hi-fi stereo with an 8-track tape.
picked a handful of long-stemmed yellow flowers

from a vacant lot.
I gave them to my Mu-dear.
She cracked a big southern smile
put the dandelions on display
like they were roses.

Orlando Taylor

A Strong Mother Growing Old

How do you look into the tired face
of the one who raised you
Molded your life and dreams as
if they were precious gold
Turn the heads not a few men in desire
Now needs a cane, umbilical cord to sustain?

Music in her voice has softened and strained.
Replaced the strong songs and deep melodies.
Expressive blues, jazz, and gospels of joy
bringing in that good old-time religion.

It is strange when your mother grows
see hands seemingly created to work
hardly able to grasp thick cheeks to kiss
hands which molded children to adults
and coaxed wounds into healing.

Mamas' hands lit a fire on hardheaded butts,
and mended tears in clothes twice too old.
Her hands have grown stiff, rheumatic
unable to grasp hold of grandchild.
Fed nine mouths, washed clothes hundreds of times
Nursed life with her breast.
Now she must be bathed and changed
a child all over again.

How do you watch a strong mother grow old?

Freedom

Freedom...Freedom
Do you feel you got your freedom
Freedom...Freedom
do you feel you got your freedom?

Black bodies falling like leaves in the fall
folks can't be bothered too busy at the mall
Can't get no justice no peace without war.

Freedom...Freedom
Do you feel you got your freedom
Freedom...Freedom
do you feel you got your freedom?

Hostile

(Inspired by Lauryn Hill's "The World is a Hustle")

The world is hostile
Children being force to fight
In wars like men
Women taken, forced to be prostitutes
And wives without truth
One's orientation is a justified subjugation.

The whole world in hostile
So many lies I can't see why
God does not cry
keep letting it all go by
The whole world is hostile
I feel like a laying down to die
When did knowing and authoring pain
Become the norm
The whole world is hostile
Television does nothing fake realities
Diminish all our humanity.

Individual proclivity outweighs
The need for reason
No longer have rights because I am
Reduced to less than a human being
The businessman on wall street and
Bankers behind walls of legislation
Destroyed millions of lives
But the black woman can't
Get a raise of five percent.

The whole world in hostile

My Scars Are My Birthmark

So many lies I can't see why
God does not cry
keep letting it all go by
The whole world is hostile
I feel like a laying down to die
When did knowing and authoring pain
Become the norm
The whole world is hostile
Television does nothing fake realities
Diminish all our humanity.

All around the world
people search for clean water
Others sleep under bridges
bullets see our butterflies
On the corners are more guns liquor
Desert storm no fresh veggies or fruit
No food for the mind and soul.

The whole world is a ghetto
Despair masked with thin layer of hope
Resigned to the lowest level of society
Numb with their hunger for a life of luxury
the whole world is a ghetto.

A dumping ground for chemical poison
Hoods no more about violence than technology
Both cause crippling diseases
Impaired to have a quality life
Schools overcrowded ill-equipped
to build a vision of tomorrow
What are we to believe?
When they kill young black men

Orlando Taylor

who could be me
I just bow my head.

The whole world is a hostile
I have no prayer that it will get better
Without burning the weeds of complacency
And those who lie and say everything is alright
The whole world is hostile.

Haiku for Haiti

in peace natives lived
blood ruled when the Catholics came
please spell rape in French

Haiku for Haiti #2

Spain enslaved with chains
France drained the land, stripped of trees
U.S. took some through

black blues in america flat

Each day the sun yawned
I tried to be a good American
Oh, each day the sun yawned
I tried to be a good American
Dey gotta a noose aroun' my soul
Can't they see the flag in this hand.

America would love me
If I straightened my hair
O', America say she loves me,
So, I straightened my hair
Still won't stand close enough to touch
'Cause the skin I'm in, ain't that fair.

Dance to the beat
Step in star-spangled time
You gotta dance to the beat
I say, step in star-spangled time
Did a shuffle on sore feet
Why y'all actin' like I committed a crime.

Lumps runnin' 'cross my head
From bumpin' on the glass ceiling
Oh, I got lumps bleedin' 'cross my head
From bumpin' on the glass ceiling
Mind tired and soul caught in limbo
Negroes grinnin' and schemin', I'm leaving.

My Scars Are My Birthmark

I did the breast stroke in a bottle
Can't feel today tomorrow is numb
I did the breast stroke down in a bottle
Can't feel today tomorrow is numb
Somebody throw the coroner's cover
The river's bottom sure to come.

Tired of living life inside exclusion
Need to find truth and sojourn on
Tired of living life inside exclusion
Need to find truth and sojourn on
This life will leave you in pieces
The Black man's burden heavy as a ton.

Now the Afrikan looking from inside
Is alright wid' me
Don't you know, the Afrikan looking from inside
Is alright wid' me
Tried too long to be this perfect citizen
Can't get freer lovin' who you meant to be.

Blessed Hate

Hate will make you strong
Hate will make you beg to be alone
Hate will burn the truth about this world into your bones
Hate will make you a sear into the heart of your enemy
Hate will is fertilizer for the journey
Hate shines a light on real friends and family
Blessed hate
I have seen through the veil
It is paper thin
Blessed hate
You are not my enemy

backlash

After 9-1-1 we see the jigs up
big brutha will soon be your mother
suckin' on liberty's tits
to drink potent political rhetoric
got negroes drunk like Hennessy and Hypnotic.

Soon all your rights will be gone
as they cart you of to war, destination unknown
terrorism is an old American trick
kidnapped nations under the name of salvation
afrikan continent spinning 'cause of missing generations
dark blood fertilizes the ocean floor and soil of plantations
broken necks and burnt bodies are fragrant offerings
on the altar to the god of hate and greed.

False freedom given and a crow named jim snatched it back
getcha anyway they can, even driving while black
not to mention legalized death squads
dressed in blue with tin shields
everyday hearing how they kill at will
they spit bullshit about moral obligation and justice
a disguise for 21st manifest destiny, and world domination.

Supported south afrikan apartheid a true menace
to society, a bizarre ride to the far side
Africans dying in tunnels and caves as the
American bird swoops down to devour
the bling-bling way before Hip-hop became mean
natives pushed, prodded, and herded
onto three inches worth of land
reservations were made but I don't know who confirmed

government urging them to make an
offering at the cross of assimilation
the only path of ascension to be a citizen.

How much more do I need to mention
so when the planes struck the towers and had them leaning
like pizza, your mind was speechless
The leftover food you feel comin' back on you
Africans in America knew what it was
others are willing to stand up and let'em know:
if you don't give a damn, we don't give a fuck.

CHAPTER FOUR

ANANSE

wisdom, creativity and the complexities of life

Short Stories

Brother's Psyche

The door opened as a young black man entered into the pool hall that doubled as a club house for a group of American street car racers he belonged to. He is about five ten, black-brown leather dyed skin, low Caesar style hair cut with millions of waves dancing around in the thick black ocean of hair. He is twenty-five, weighs about 190 lbs., with oval eyes cut to points in the inner corners, with medium pomegranate-colored lips. His eyes are surrounded by bushy caterpillars for eyebrows, and long playful lashes that look like they could wave in the wind. He favors pictures of Egyptian men drawn on pyramid walls. There are small diamond stud earrings in each ear, and on his left arm, a tattoo of a violet dragon spitting light blue, orange, and yellow flames. The tail coils around his left shoulder and wraps around his arm until its head breathes out flames in the middle of the forearm. He has on indigo-colored jeans, a gray "wife-beater," with a wallet chain, metal wrist bands, and blue and yellow tennis shoes. He walks easily to the bar, nodding to some friends inside the bar who look his way. There are a lot of people inside for three o'clock on a Saturday afternoon. There are no women, because they are not allowed except for special meetings and Sundays. The young men inside are all black, confident, with a taste of negative excitement swirling around on their palettes.

"Wassup, Perell, ain't seen you in a few weeks? What you drankin' on?" came the tall, light brown bartender with his son's name tattooed on his neck. He was smooth-skinned in the face except for a light mustache and eyebrows. He is about fifteen years older than Pernell, but he could easily pass for someone younger.

"Aye Ronnie, give me a double shot of whiskey, and a tall mug of whatever's on tap," he returned calmly. "There are a lot more people here for a Saturday afternoon," he continued.

"Don't even try it bro, you know like I do what today is," Ronnie said with grin. He continued, "So you might as well go on back to the circle to see if your name comes up."

Pee threw back his shot quickly, and downed a full gulp of his beer. With his beer mug in hand, he paid his bill and walked away to the right of the bar toward a group of members gathered in the back with his beer in hand. As he approached, the others were joining in what looked like a regular game of craps, but it was something much more. As Perell walks back, he sees Carman playing spades at one table and by his loud mouth, his team was beating their opponent's ass. He gave Carman a nod with his head and kept on moving slowly toward the others.

"Perell!" someone called. "Perell, I know yo' punk ass hears me!" the voice insisted. The voice coming from his left was Mann, a fearless brother who never knew when to quit when it came to getting into some shit. He is a true midnight colored Black African American male. He often claimed that the darkness of his skin made him a pure blood. I never contradicted him because I wasn't interested in a useless argument that would ensue. Mann was same height as Perell, but a little smaller in weight. He wore braids of one style or another in his hair most of the time.

"Hey, black ass mutha fucka; I thought you and Ronnie were still having a lover's quarrel?" I said loudly back to him.

"Y'all must have kissed and made up in the last week." Perell said in earnest.

"Fuck you!" Mann returned slow, and loudly, but with a small laugh.

"I see yo' ass is here too, kin- folk," he continued.

"I wanted to see who was gon' be next from the group," Mann finished.

"Well it looks like a lot people wanted to see", said Perell sarcastically, "and since my name might come up, I figured I'd show my pretty face for y'all."

They moved closer to one another and clasped their right hands together with understanding. "If you are chosen," Mann said, 'my money is on you bro.'"

Perell, looked into Mann's face and knew he was sincere.

"It had better be, or else I'd have to start dating yo' moms again!"

Mann just looked, shook his head, and said "Go to hell." Then he walked back to where he was sitting.

Perell continued walking to back where the group was stilled gathered. Some people were sitting in chairs, while others were crowded standing around behind them. The table was loud with conversation, and laughter. It seemed to be all the usual people hanging out in the club, but it had been a while since Perell had been out there. He was at ease though he had been away from this group that was like family. He is even looking forward to seeing who would be chosen.

Perell thought, *I hope if either of us gets chosen, it will be me.*

Suddenly he hears, "Stop looking so serious, you know you like this place and the attention."

Perell didn't look around because the voice was coming from inside his head and it wasn't his conscience. "Would you please get out of my head?" Perell said returning the thought, "Anyway, I thought you said I was cuter when I was serious."

There were a few minutes before an answer came back. "I don't lie, so it's true," the voice returned. "Your arms all shiny and stuff in that wife beater, makes me wanna throw you down…" the voice trailed off as Perell spoke aloud.

"Quit trippin', and I told you to get out of…!" Perell said.

"Who you talkin' to bro, I can come here as much as I want. My Uncle runs the place."

Perell looked around to his left and then down and saw who it was interrupting his thoughts.

The deep voice was coming from the chest of a young man just a little younger than himself, light brown in color, with a bald head. He was much shorter than Perell, maybe five feet five, with a swimmer's build. "Oh, my bad, Twon," Perell responded. "I got caught in my own thoughts." he finished.

"I spoke to Ronnie when I came in", he said easily, "and he didn't mention you were here."

"I know," said Twon, "he still mad I wrecked the Cutlass last week."

"Damn," said Perell shocked. "I tried to buy it off him last summer and he said no to me quick. I'm surprised he didn't buss yo' head open!"

"He tried, heh," Twon said, "but being small makes it easy sometimes for you to get away from big man."

Perell put his left arm around Twon's shoulder like he was the older brother of the two. "So, when are you going to join the club, bro?" He said tapping Twon in the middle of his chest with his left hand.

"I'm still thinking about it, but there ain't another clique I'd rather be in."

"So, when you gon' make this happen?" asked Perell.

"Soon, I guess. Are you gonna sponsor me through?" returned Twon.

Perell thought for a moment, squeezed Twon's shoulder and said, "No problem, I got you, but you have to get in on the first try. If you don't, I won't help you a second time."

Twon, looked down on the floor, and then up at Perell as if in deep thought. He then nodded his head and said, "I can handle it."

"Good, you'll be fine, just call me when you want to start," Perell spoke softly. Perell began to walk toward the back to see if he would be called next even though he was trying hard not to care. But he does and anxiety is rising in him just as quick as his heart rate.

He has never lost before, and those who are left among the unchosen are just as good as he is now. It will be one of the toughest matches he's faced, he was thinking, but what's this life about without some crazy risks?

"Hey, what's going on back there?" Perell asked the voice. "Have they picked the first name yet?"

"Wow, you changed your mind quick," came the voice with obvious sarcasm, "a few minutes ago you told me to get outta yo' head, now you want me to give you an update?"

"Whatever, either you know or you don't!" returned Perell in a strong voice.

"Yeah, you were right bro; you do look cuter when you are serious." the voice said. "But to answer the question," the voice replied in a regular tone, "no, they ha- ven't, but they will in a few minutes. I think they waitin' on Rennie to comeback from takin' a piss."

Rennie is the current head of the club. Nobody else wanted to lead, including me, so he got the position by default, but who cares. Rennie is cool headed, and works hard to keep our club known as one of the best car clubs around. He's a good driver and a level headed brother that several women would fight over. He is tall, burnt brown color, with gray eyes, and dusty-brown hair. He is what most would describe as a true red-bone brother. He does not have a very muscular physique, but he is country-boy thick, with a flat stomach. He is the kind of guy that doesn't notice the shadow he casts over people, or how being around makes some people jealous. It does help that he has five years on a lot of the guys in the club including me. Rennie always has something good to say even when you disagree with him. Which I like, because it makes you feel like you talking to an older relative in your family. So, when people are selected next; he is the one who approves the selection and overseas the race. Each person in the club must drag with a club member every three years to maintain your place, and tenure in the group. It's a way of keeping us all sharp, knowing who's improved, and where we may need to improve among our membership. So, I had to do it about three years after I joined at the age of seventeen. I guess it's my time all over again. Which, I don't mind, because I know what I can do.

Rennie walked back from behind Perell and playfully bumps him with his shoulder. "Come on Rennie, man, and Pee get yo' black ass out his way," shouted Maurice, the biggest and loudest mother fucker in the club.

Everybody around him and few others near him laughed loudly. He was trying to be funny because he knew I was one of the people who could be chosen next.

"Ok, let's get this shit going, so we can all get back to drankin' or going home," said Rennie. "And from the smell in here some of y'all need to hurry up and get home to wash yo' asses," he said matter-of-factly.

"Maurice, waiting on you to wash his personally," Perell chimed in, "aintcha big boy!" Folks were laughing but those right near Maurice just snickered a little bit, or turned away to laugh in their hand. Maurice stood up and point toward Perell with fake seriousness. "I tol' you a few weeks ago, Pee, to quit playing with me", he retorted, "looks like I'm gon' have to beat you like yo' grandmother used to with the back of her fist."

He pressed his fist up to his lips and then pointed at Perell with the same hand. "Now that we got all the foolishness out the way, Juju, hand me the dice so I can shoot to see who is next?" asked Rennie. Juju reached up under the table and pull out three silver colored die with red dots on them. These were only used for these dice, nothing else. It was one of the only rules we had in our club. Rennie grabbed them from Juju's hand

and began to shake the in his hand. Each person in the group had a number assigned to them. When it was called you had to race your car against another club member in an area chosen by Rennie at random. There are only thirty people in the club and new members are allowed in only after someone dies, leaves the group, or we elected to increase the number of members.

Rennie threw the dice on the table and rolled a five, a six, and a two. This was not Perell's number, but another club member. He immediately stood up excited his number had been called. It was Quincy, and Perell was not pleased. Quincy was a couple of inches shorter than Perell, skin somewhere between sunset and night, and a small body out of a muscle magazine. His eyes were black and looked as tight and narrow Khoisan people. He had a mustache and handful of hair on his chin that was a couple of inches in length, and small bob-style afro.

"Why you looking all upset?" asked someone's voice inside Perell's head.

"I'm not upset, just a little concerned about racing," responded Perell.

"Are you afraid of getting beat, boy?" the voice asked coyly.

"Hell no," Perell responded forcefully, "ain't too many better than me anyway, including you."

"So, let's see what happens with the next number," he finished.

Everyone waited as Rennie shook his hand for the dice to roll for the next driver. The first die was a three, the next was a two, and last a three. "Well, you got yo' wish bro," came the voice quickly, "too bad you gon' loose." Perell made sure all knew Quincy was there by panning the room with his eyes and stopping on Quincy. Most people knew he didn't like Pee, but he couldn't get around Perell.

Perell was a favorite son in the group being the first to join at age seventeen. He could almost do no wrong. Rennie stood up and roughly made his way toward Quincy and then Perell. He grabbed them both by their forearms and made the announcement of where it was going down at for the drag race. "The race goes down this evening on Old Talty Road near the cliffs hanging over Trinity River. It's the usual bet; the loser forfeits his car for six months, and has to work the door at events for the next three months."

"When you lose don't worry, I'll come and pick you up anytime you need sexy," came the voice talking to him. "It will be nice having Mr. Sexy Baby, riding on the passenger side," the voice finished with a laugh.

"You know what," thought Perell and grinned, "If I win, then you will have to cook Sunday dinner for me for the whole time I got the car."

The voice was silent for about a few minutes. Perell turned to face Quincy, and gave him a pound.

"I'm down with that, but as bad as you want to," came the voice, "you ain't gon' be eating my cooking, even though I can burn!"

Perell left the area where Rennie and the others were and headed back to the bar where Ronnie was still serving.

"Ron, let me have another shot of Jack and draft beer, man."

Ronnie looked at him sideways out the corner of his eye and said, "Are you sure you wanna do that Pee?"

Perell stared him in the eyes without hesitation. It was clear he was upset that Ronnie had even asked such a question. Ronnie slid the drink down to him and a few seconds later came Perell's beer. "Thanks," said Perell flatly.

As he was finishing his beer, he could see Quincy making his way outside as if to say he was ready, even though it was not time. So, Perell finished his beer and calmly went outside as well. Others noticed and followed suit trying not to look obvious, but somehow it couldn't be helped.

Quincy was standing outside on the sidewalk in front of the club trying not to look like he was waiting on Perell. Perell could see Quincy's wide shoulders, as he came out the door, looking confident to the casual observer. "Ain't no sense in waiting any longer," said Perell.

"I know, Pee", said Quincy calmly looking sideways at Perell, "So give me your keys now and we can avoid you crying later."

Perell said nothing, but snickered. He started walking with firm footfalls toward his car without looking back. He got to his car, an aqua green 1968 Chevrolet Camaro with white leather interior and super-white racing stripes on the hood of the car. He had modified the doors to make them smoother, by moving the door handles from the side, to the roof. He had to press downward and the driver side door opened quietly, and closed with a heavy thud. Perell started the engine and it purred deep and heavy like Barry White's voice. Not obnoxiously loud noise, but like the fine-tuned voice of a bass singer. He leaned out of his window, and called to Quincy.

"Come on Q," he called playfully, like a kid trying to get his friend to come out and play, "I'll meet you out on Talty Road in thirty-minutes."

Quincy smiled and started trotting for his Orange 1969 GTO as Perell drove pass hanging out his window winking at Quincy.

Quincy's car had dark blue cloth interior and gold chrome trim around the wheel wells, front grill, and the rear bumper. It growled loud like lion announcing "this is my territory" when he started it up and you knew this would not be an ordinary race. All the people who came out to see simultaneously let out loud shouts and whoops as they headed for their cars enroute to the drag race destination. Behind the bar Ronnie said a silent prayer while pretending to dry another beer glass.

Despite Perell's excited nature he was not all together calm. He couldn't help the feeling that his life would change dramatically after he won this race. Perell drove in silence all the way to the spot chosen for the race. He listened to the rhythm of the car's tires rolling across the cracks in the asphalt streets, the engine's rumble, and the scenes whisking by in his peripheral vision. Despite his deepest feelings he was smiling the last few miles before arriving at the place.

As Quincy and the rest of the people were coming in the distance, not yet close enough to see, Perell made a move. He revved up his car's engine and did several figure eights in sight of the coming crowd. There was thick tire smoke in the air nearly rendering him invisible and deep black skid marks mapping the path of all his tire's violent twists and turns. When his car stopped on the road, he had positioned it so that it was sideways with the driver's side facing the coming crowd.

His right arm was gripping the stirring wheel while his left arm hung out the window. The tension in the muscles of his arm made the purple dragon look as if it was going to leap from his arm. There is the stare of defiance in his eyes, and the right side of his mouth is curled in a menacing grin of anticipation.

As the smoke dissipates, he can see Quincy in front like a surfer riding a wave. Quincy stopped about six feet from his car with the front end facing Perell. He then began to drive around Perell in several erratic, yet controlled circles.

The rear end of his GTO shakes left to right as he completes his turns. Once Quincy was done, he stopped in his original position in front of Perell. The only noise came from their cars; the witnesses weren't say anything. The dust and smoke he generated has not dissipated yet. Quincy then rolls up the passenger side window which has a deep dark tint, then turns to look directly into Perell's eyes. His stone face reveals nothing until he suddenly come forward and turns the car so that the driver side of his car is parallel to Perell's driver side. No one could see what was happening or being said because Perell had also rolled up his passenger side window too.

"See, I told you, you are cuter when you have that serious look on your face," said Quincy.

"Well, maybe after all this," began Perell, "you can throw me down like you suggest- ed earlier. Be careful," Quincy finished.

They spoke not with words, but with the power of their thoughts. They've known ever since they met, that communication within their minds was possible. In fact, it was this power that drove them to each other giving them two secrets to share between them.

No matter which one of us wins, we both win today,
Quincy thought with sincerity. They then clasped left hands
and pulled their faces toward one another and kissed strongly;
sharing their lips and tongues ferociously for several.

"Let's get this over with quickly", calmly said Perell.

Perell made his move so that his car faces the cliff and
Quincy followed his lead. All the club members who came to
watch had arrived at the spot and were cheering so loud there
was competition with the roar of the cars' engines.

Rennie stepped from the crowd with a bullhorn in hand,
and said, "Brothers, on your mark, get set..." he paused
purposely to make things even tenser before he uttered the last
word, "Go!"

Both cars lurched forward immediately. And as the
RPMs went higher, the wheels spent out of control, and the
engines wrestled to stay bolted to their chassis'. Perell glanced
easily at Quincy for a second just to admire the look on his face
as he himself, drives with no emotion, while the left arm still
dangled coolly out the side of his car. Quincy just looked ahead
getting intoxicated off the swiftness of the scenery approaching
then retreating from the sides of his car. At one moment Perell
is ahead, the next Quincy has taken the lead, only to be
surpassed by Perell again.

This happened several times as they approached the cliff.
At a designated point on the road, marked by a large bolder on

the side, they were to begin breaking, because at their speed they would need enough distance to stop without going over the cliff. Maurice had already positioned himself near the rock to determine a winner.

As they approached it, Quincy made another move forward, but the rear of his car began to swerve, so he started to gently break and turn the front wheels to compensate. His breaks were not working properly, and the GTO, which loves speed, responded very little to the pressure he applied.

At that moment Perell heard Quincy's voice in his head, "Pee, my breaks are not working, but I'm going to win this race!"

Perell was stunned for a moment letting the reality of his words hit him. "What the fuck are saying?!" was all he could return.

At that moment they cross the imagery line near the bolder and Quincy's car edges out Perell's by an inch. Maurice could see who won but could not tell there was a problem because neither of them slowed down once they passed the line.

Perell quickly moves his car closer to Quincy's almost touching his passenger side to Quincy's driver side. "Q, see if you can pull your car closer and crawl into mine before we get to the cliff!," shouted Perell into Quincy's mind. Quincy began to pull his car closer to Perell's and ease himself up and through his car window. Perell couldn't watch him because he needed to keep his car straight, but also because he didn't want Quincy to see the fear creeping into his face.

The cliff was getting nearer and Perell couldn't see Quincy's progress. Quincy had steered his car so close that Perell could smell the car fresher wafting from the open window. He kept his right hand on the steering wheel, and the left hand using the roof for leverage as he lifted his butt onto his car's window edge, and then his knees up level with his stomach. With his hand still on the wheel, he ducked his head down inside of Perell's passenger window. Then he let go the steering wheel and desperately used both hands to pull himself inside and using the window frame. Just as he did the GTO kissed the side of the Perell's Camaro causing sparks to fly. Perell applied the brakes firmly and prayed the car would not begin to spin out of control.

Quincy's car kept driving forward without him like the scene from a movie. Perell still didn't look at Quincy, but grabbed him closer with his right arm as Quincy's head almost fell into his lap. Before the GTO leapt from the asphalt into the air, Perell turned the wheel of his car and caused it to turn to the right bringing the passenger's side parallel to the cliff's edge. Meanwhile, Quincy's car smashed head first into the side cliffs on the opposite side causing and immediate explosion and a shower of fiery parts down below. Perell's car though parallel had slid off the edge so that both wheels on the passenger side were now hanging off the side of cliff's edge in the air. Perell's chest was heaving hard and steady as Quincy began lifting himself up. "This car is going to go over too," Perell said stiffly. "I am going to open the door on my side easily and slowly, and then we gotta quickly get out, you hear me!" he said looking down at Quincy.

Quincy nodded his head and said matter-a-factly, "I won, you owe me a car," he finished in between hurried breaths. Perell opened his door and with his right arm hooked under Quincy's he lunged out the door and using his left arm to guide and pull them.

Quincy used his feet to push with all his might against the car's interior to help propel them out and onto the ground. And as they landed on the ground the Camaro tilted and made its plunge to the ground a hundred feet below or more. They had both landed on Perell's back who patted Quincy's right shoulder and said, "You owe me your life and a car, bro."

They both laughed feeling the movement of their bodies against one another. Perell leaned his head up and kissed Quincy's forehead and they got up slowly, looked each other in the eyes and hugged like lover's who hadn't seen one another in a hundred years. They were covered in dust, scrapes, and scratches on their arms, face and torso.

At that moment Maurice walked upon them and said, "You mother fuckers must be blessed by the gods, 'cause ain't no way neither of you should still be alive!"

Neither Quincy nor Perell said anything mentally or verbally, they already knew his statement was true in more than one way. And the next moment the three of them started laughing nervously, but honestly.

Family Reunion: Water from Clay Vessels

It was not a cold day and the sky was usually clear, the sun decided today no one would go without seeing him. There are young children running around screaming in glee. Others are working with elders to pre- pare for the day. One man, not young, not old, is standing on the front porch as family arrived. He looked familiar like I should know him, but I couldn't say his name.

As my dad pulled up to the curb and then into the gravel drive, I saw him closer, and he looked like an older version of my dad. As I looked at him, he turned and looked at me for a few seconds, then smiled so genuinely, I burst into the biggest smile too. It was like I saw someone I needed to see. A man who was there, just waiting on me to step forward.

My father exited the car and looked at him with both a wariness and pride. My father could have been his son. My dad, walked up the drive-way toward him and his gaze turned from non-committal, to a smirk, until it became a smile that looked like he is seeing something beautiful for the first time. They embraced, and as their chests came together there was the sound of a drum. They held each other longer than I had seen two men touch before.

"Nephew, you look good. So glad to see you."

There were a several heavy pats on the back and this man turned to me. My father is his nephew, so that means he's my uncle too.

He turned to me and held out his hand, "Hey, little king, what's your name?"

I looked at my father who smiled and the look on his face said, "Go ahead and introduce yourself, boy!" So, I did.

I cleared my throat and held out my hand, "My name is Raury, who are you?"

He shook it firm and like he wouldn't let go. There were callouses in it, but there was a gentleness coming through as he held it for a few moments.

"Call me," he began, "Uncle Rucker." He then jerked me forward along my arm into his torso with a little force.

My head bumped into his firm but yielding stomach and he patted me on my back several times. And he continued, "We've never met before. Blame that on your dad, because I do."

Uncle Rucker's face changed slightly as he looked at pop, Jessie. It was a quick glance of disappointment but then it was gone, and with his arm jealously around my shoulder he ushered use further into the sea of people. A sea filled many colors and babies, children, youth, and the elders.

My uncle looked down at me and said, "You may not
know most of these people, but these are your people. Never be
afraid of them."

I believed him because listening to his words
reverberated inside his torso. It was like music bouncing against
the internal walls of a speaker before finding me. The words
made me feel like no truer words had been spoken and I smile
like I was two years old eating candy for the first time. We
walked past so many people who were mostly genuinely glad to
see Uncle Rucker. Only a few smiles faded quickly like butter
sliding off a hot biscuit. He looked down at me and then to the
left at my father who looked nervous as he approached a large
group of older folks.

"You'll learn little king, that sometimes you even have to
ignore certain family members in order to get things done. Still
no need to ever be afraid of them." He paused and let me go for
a second to speak and greet a few people.

One woman came up to us, "I know you ain't walking by
here and not give Aunt Willa a hug?"

My dad quickly, moved to hug her and then she looked
at Uncle Rucker, then me. "Who is this handsome little fella?"
She looked at me, then leaned down and kissed my forehead
before pop could answer. "Never mind, I see your daddy in
your face now." The kiss was warm and she smelled flowers

originated with her. A butterfly landed on her hair as she finished talking.

As we came near, in the distance a large tree that looked like it had been around longer than our family came into my view. The back on the tree looked like it had been hardened with molten rock and at certain places it looked like the tree had sprouted small horns. Most of the arms stretched horizontally to the left and right, and then upward. The arms thick, strong, looking like a dancer reaching up until there is no more upward. The shade the tree created was cool and complete as the canopy of leaves above allowed virtually no sun light to lay on the ground. I remember how pleasantly cool it was under the tree. Thinking back on this moment, it felt like a dream I had, where the whole family was there surrounding pits cooking, games, and food. I couldn't shake the feeling that this is a dream and I was living someplace back in time where we lived on a simple land and people built their own homes. In the dream I was hurrying to get outside because I was late getting up and several older men and women shook their heads, as I ran by not to be late. But, in the dream I could never see the man's face, but now it feels like it had to have been Uncle Rucker.

Everyone greeted each other in different but loving ways as me, my dad, and Uncle Rucker made to the shade tree.

By the time we finished our greetings more people came to the area, some, seemed like they came up just to meet Uncle Rucker. When I looked at my dad watching him, he had a look of admiration on his face that vacillated between worry as well. Uncle Rucker, was in the zone as he greeted people never looking exhausted but growing more eager and happier as people spoke to him. The greetings ceased as great granddaddy Jessie stood to say grace. Some prayed others just stood or held their own hands and were glad the praying was done so that they could serve themselves.

As people were finishing, one of my older cousins, about nineteen, said something that seemed to upset several elders in the family including Uncle Rucker, who looked in his direction and shook his head. His name was Keenan, but we called him Kee-Kee for short. He directed a comment as Uncle Rucker, but many felt it was for all the elders.

"I don't know why people keep telling me I need to do something with my life! I am. I don't know one here doing much either. We don't have any doctor's or lawyer in our family. Don't seem like folks done too much before me!" He stopped and looked around.

For a young man he was not small. He was the color of an acorn shell, tall, lean but not lanky. Built like LeBron James, but in a body fifteen years younger.

My grandad, Lee, started to speak, "Boy, you just ..."

Uncle Rucker looked at grand- daddy and held up his hand and he sat back down looking cross at Kee-Kee. Keenan opened his mouth but his moth- er shook her head. I didn't know that he was the youngest son of Aunt Tracy, Uncle Rucker's oldest sister.

Uncle Rucker, got up and walk toward Keenan who looked like he was preparing to dodge a swat to the head from my uncle. "These family gatherings we have, have never been about filling our guts until we pop. It is a time to reconnect, rejuvenate, and for those older to inject history, wisdom, knowledge, into the young ones."

He turned and looked at Kee-Kee and said, "That means you as well! You have your responsibility toward young ones like your cousin Raury and us to you!"

There was silence for what seemed like an hour but it was more like five seconds. As usual Kee-Kee had to have the last word.

"Well, I don't understand, if I am supposed to do for the younger ones as you say, why someone didn't do this for me? I didn't need it anyway just like they don't! Besides once you out here ain't nobody got much to offer us."

I think I heard Uncle Rucker's neck crack as it snapped around to look at Kee-Kee.

"And that is your problem," he began. "You think giving, means money, and money only!"

He walked over to Kee-Kee so he could look him in the face directly. "Before you graduated, like the others, someone sat down with you at some point to help you figure out what the hell you wanted to do next."

Rucker moves even closer, within one foot of Kee-Kee. "And I know for sure Uncle Ephraim talked to you. But you didn't think he had much to offer and you didn't follow through on anything you were advised about."

He paused for a moment and looked at Aunt Claire then to Kee-Kee. "Now you feeling the pressure since your mother is ready for you to grow up and move out!"

Kee-Kee looked like he had been hit the face and then he looked at Aunt Claire.

"There is no reason for you nor anyone to be where you are now with all these people around you. Think! Ask questions! If you don't feel like you are getting what you need from someone, guess what, there are other folks here who are all too willing to help."

"What have I always said? Do you remember?"

There was a pause and Kee-Kee looks on the ground. "I'll remind you. You are right we do not always have a bunch of money or wealth to share, but what we lack there we make up in other ways. Do you think we wouldn't if we had it? What kind of people do you think we are, son? You have to be unbreakable in this world, because we are all damaged, but we are not broken. No matter how they bend you, you cannot break, or you and those depending on you are done! Do you hear me!"

"My suggestion is, if you need some help then you had better open your damn mouth, or just shut the hell up! Because your too young to be walking around here like you running anything. Most of the time you when talking it sounds like you got diarrhea of the mouth. Just a well spring of bull coming out!"

Uncle Rucker paused for a moment and took out a handkerchief to wipe is mouth and forehead. Then he continued. "You haven't taken even two seconds to determine if what you say is real or not. Always talking 'bout being real! Real what?! Lost?"

More silence as Rucker's voice echoes and other elders nod or grunt in agreement. "You have to identify that thing you want to do so bad your heart feels like it going to commit suicide if you cannot get it done. Which means nothing nor no one is going to stop you! Ask you cousin, Arya? She could see it but she knew she had to get to Houston so she could fulfill her desire of being a graphic artist/designer. So, the question you need to ask yourself is... "What is it I can't live without doing, and I will you help you with that? Any of us will!"

There is a bit of silence and Uncle Rucker shakes his head looks down and then begins to walk away from the crowd in silence and heavy steps toward the line between his land and the neighbors. He walks for about a quarter of a mile before he arrives at a place to rest for a moment. He looked over and waived to one his neighbor, an elderly woman and then a younger man came out looked and waved as well.

The woman nodded her head and laughed and the young man moved toward him.

"The young ones are more stubborn than I remember, Baba. What are you going to do?"

Rucker hangs his head for a moment and then looks off in the distance for a moment. When he comes back from thought, the man has come close to him. "Have you ever thought that maybe the time is now?" she asked looking intently into Rucker's eyes.

"Yes, but days like this make me afraid it will never happen."

"Sometimes," the man began, "you have to push them in the right direction."

Rucker doesn't move, exhales, then he talks as if he is exhausted. "Well then, there is no better time than the present." They both begin to walk toward the elder woman still sitting on the porch.

Nightfall has come to the gathering and there are people looking for Uncle Rucker including me and my dad, Jessie. We all began to look. I remembered seeing him go speak to the elders next door.

"Dad," I started hurriedly, "I saw Unc walk over there and speak to his neighbors. But he never came back."

My dad, looked in their direction and then back to the others. "Come with me." He walked over to his sister, Aunt Yuma, and told her what was going on and that he and I were going next door. "If we do not come back, you know what to do."

She hugged him, then said, "You know I do." She reached down and hugged me too and we off to the neighbors.

As we approached the home, it was larger up close than it did from away and it was medium blue color on the outside. My father approached and knock on the door. In few moments a woman came to the door. "Hello," the woman began, "how can I help you brothers?"

My dad stepped forward on the porch and into the screen door. "Sorry to bother you so late, ma'am, but my uncle came pass and we have not seen him since." He stopped and looked around. "Have you seen him in the last hour or so?"

The woman nods her head, "Yes, baby, he was here but he's gone now."

My uncle pressed, "Did he say anything about where he was going?"

"He just said it was time the young ones begin to understand their role in the family. That was the last I saw of him."

My dad looked at her suspiciously then pulled me closer to his side with his hand. "Thank you, and if he comes back here tell him we are waiting for him at the house."

She nodded and we left the porch. As we walked away she called after us, "Knowing him, it won't take him long."

We return to the others. But what we didn't know is that my uncle had been taken to a place where he could get the answers he had been seeking with respect to family and how to make sure he could assure our families security for centuries to come. To that end the man who was there had taken my uncle to perform a ceremony my uncle hoped would give him the insight he needed.

The process included the consumption of a special herb that helped him "see." To complete the process, he had to be buried for a day he told us. It was symbolic of dying to the old ways and opening oneself to the new. We worried because all we learned was from him. But we had to find him and we did. But it was something wondrous to go through.

I had remembered something dad had said when we were looking for clues in the house. It brought back the moment we met uncle out front. It was like all the air around me stop, but the world was spinning slowly.

"Wait, dad. It's you! You know where Uncle Rucker is at."

My father wrinkled his face in great pain and anguish. "Boy, how. We went looking for him…"

I quickly started in, "Uncle Rucker said you were not where you are supposed to be!"

My father shook his head several time. "Raury, you're not making sense. I became who I am, what I am suppose…

"No. There was something else once, correct?"

"What?" dad said.

I looked at him as if to ask him to look deeper than he had before by raising my eyebrows. And in his face, there was a light all of a sudden and he snapped his head toward Keenan. "I remember, for years until my late teens I wanted to own multiple farms to help feed our people better. I think that is what uncle was talking about. But I don't understand how this helps us."

He stopped and asked Keenan a question. "Do you know where great grand papa's diving rod is at?"

"Shit, it has to be here somewhere because you know no one else would have thought it worth anything.", returned Keenan.

My father ran from the house like a rocket trying to follow a heat signature straight to the shed and I and Keenan kept up with him as best we could. By the time we caught him in the shed he was ruffling through boxes and looking in corners. Then he found it further in the dark, behind an old cedar chest.

"Got it!" he said. And then went outside. "Ancestors help me find him; he is very important to us."

I was confused by it all. "Pop, how can to rods help us find him?"

"He is a man," I continued, "not water!"

Then my father looked contemplative for a moment and walked slowly out the shed. "Our uncle is like the water in the family, trying to get us to drink from our past all the time, even when we are reluctant."

Keenan scratched his head, and said, "So if we see him as water, you'll be able to find him?"

"I am not sure, but we will give a try. It's all we got." Jessie finished.

So, he walked outside and around near Uncle Rucker had been last and the rods jerked him forward and continued to guide dad until the three of us came upon a mound of dirt and the rods shot from my father's hand into the mounds.

"Here. Kee-Kee can you go get two shovels so we can see if he is in there!?"

When Keenan came back, he had two more cousins his age and my dad's brother Noah. They all took turns, including me. Then when my father, who was last to dig, hits something, they all frantically dig with their hands until the box is unearthed and Uncle Rucker is removed.

"Why were you in here? I don't understand!" exclaimed Uncle Noah.

Rucker touched Noah's shoulder and asked him to help out and back to the house. The night was quiet and cool and no one said anything. Once inside, we got uncle something to drink and two of the men help clean him up some before he talked to us.

"I am not old nor am I young either. I had to do something to see who is going to be responsible for the family when I and others are gone. I... because it didn't feel like anyone was getting and stepping up."

My father shook his head and looked at me. "Raury did. He helped me remember something about myself that I had forgotten." He spoke. "At one time all I wanted to do was find a way to feed our people. And I guess I forgot that."

"You young men must be the water in the family that encourages and nourishes us all. Not above your sisters, but in unison with them."

I never forgot that day or the powerful lessons I learned that helped bring us closer and now we understood where, when, what we needed to be.

Book of 144,000

I started these words before, but until now I haven't been able to write a coherent account for those who were born here, and for those who have forgotten. It has been more than seven hundred years since I was taken or saved from my home planet, we called Earth. The world eventually burned like an out-of-control forest fire. Before leaving, I watched people spontaneously go insane and violate themselves or others in ways that made me feel I was on the verge of joining them. So, I will attempt to put it in words the events that forced us to a new home.

It was fall 2154 and I was living in Jackson, Mississippi in a loft I had recently purchased over on State Street. It was nice because at night I would escape to the roof and look out over the city like a god looking over creation. About a hundred years earlier Jackson had begun a strong revitalization and city growth project. The city had finally transformed into a true southern metropolis, and twenty years later, it had become one that equaled Atlanta, Houston, and Miami.

I opened a store where I sold handmade wood furniture. I was designing and carving pieces by hand and selling them out my previous loft. I had sold several pieces earlier in the year and used the money to finance my move to a more spacious loft. The patrons who bought my earlier works told their friends and this had created a nice demand for my work. I did my research to make some pieces which had varying ethnic appeal. I felt like I had found my niche, my space, and purpose among my community. But, in the end, I guess it was all just a passing of time.

The world outside Jackson, what can I say it had many troubles that most, including myself, tried to forget. Sometimes, I would go three weeks or more at a time without watching or listening to world news. It was always filled with redundant depressing stories of death, epidemics, and wars. Racism still pressed heavily and of course, this always leads to discrimination of one kind or another. I felt as if I could write the news and mankind's history for that matter without seeing anything on the television again. So, looking back now, I should have paid attention to it but didn't. Yet, given the events that got me here, I do not think it would have mattered.

China had successfully penetrated and developed the South American markets. They were no longer considered a country on the move, but one that had arrived as an economic and political force that no one could avoid. The China's official languages were Cantonese, Mandarin, and Spanish.

The United States was still an economic power, but not on the scale as it had been at the beginning of the twenty-first century. The continent of Africa was still in the US's and other Western country's sights for exploitation of its natural resources. To the surprise of the Western world, many African countries had banned together to consolidate their military power, and economic abilities to sustain themselves without outside financial influence from the World Bank. But, by the middle of the 21st-century, China, India, and Venezuela were in a race to see who would become the planets next major economy to influence the world globally. By 2079, Garissa, Timbuktu, Cairo, Abuja, Nakuru, and Kumasi were now major world cities.

This all happened by the fall of 2167, but I may have some of the details incorrect, but the truth of the events I am clear about. It doesn't matter anymore, I guess. I cannot bring back the earth or any of the people who did not see or deserve the end they were given. This is the backdrop right before it all happened. In a flash, a broken moment, the time span it takes to blink twice it was gone. There was no major announcements or news flash on television. The thousands of us who survived learned later that Earth had been observed by beings from another galaxy for the past 230 years. They are a humanoid like people, whose average height I estimate to be 7' or more. These aliens are a lean species with what we would call swimmers build or the physique of most basketball players. Their facial features almost mirror ours, but their noses are less pronounced, lacking a bridge. Their eyes are narrow, with three inner irises. Most have either gray or light brown eyes. They have large hands with seven fingers on each which, gives them a very strong grip and are medium to deep blue skin color. They call themselves the Pykor from a planet called Mzyloria nearly thirty light years beyond Sirius B. The Pykor came to study humanities past, present, and predict when humans might reach their level of intelligence.

The reason why the Pykorians came was because there was a problem in their home galaxy. The nearest star to Mzyloria was set to supernova in roughly three hundred years from their first visit to Earth. Additionally, many of their people were dying from a type of cancer from the harmful rays emanating from that star. In some cases, it had caused them to become sterile, and a mutation in their DNA was causing many stillborn children. At the rate of exposure to the harmful rays, their species would be extinct before the stars implosion. So, they began to search for a species they could cohabitate and procreate with to keep their species alive. Humanity, they believed, could be the answer to their needs, but from earlier studies, they knew it would be an unavoidably slow process. So, they sent out scientists first, and then later other people masked as humans so that they could study us.

They studied the histories of all earth peoples including some we had had very little contact with by the 22nd century. From the data that was gathered in the first one hundred years, they found humanity to be historically redundant, violent, and self-destructive to themselves and other species. They were about to give up on themselves, but our many achievements in science, medicine, and engineering showed the real promise of our species. They wanted to help us learn how to get beyond our petty issues and to use our technology to share natural resources. We needed to help other people worldwide too so that the typical problems of everyday life and disease were no longer common, but a rarity among us all. It was only then we could focus on improving the future outlook for mankind. The closest thing I have found to this in their language is the word letcrimun which roughly means "rising above common existence," or enlightenment as many have called it. So, they lived among us with no malicious intent as ordinary people hoping in 230 years we would change dramatically for the better. It should have been enough time for us to change, but maybe I know nothing at all about my own kind.

They chose various ethnic groups, genders, and cultures to live amongst to understand us completely. Among the Pykor, what we call sexual orientation does not exist. They believe a "Tjoka, ti pun tjoka", which means, "A spirit is attracted to a spirit." Therefore, they have no word for heterosexual, bisexual, or homosexual. Those who want to create a life do so as they please. And those who do not or cannot, are viewed the same as everyone else in their society.

In the end, they had several of their people live as gay and bi-sexual humans on the planet. One of the many Pykorians who lived as a human in this way was one called Jhenda. He would be viciously murdered, and this act became the fire that swallowed the planet.

Jhenda lived in northern Nigeria among the Hausa people. He followed their customs as closely as any twenty-five-year-old Hausa man would in the current century (although Jhenda was 157 human years old). He lived quietly and appeared to those who knew him to be a humble, intelligent man who would be successful in life. The Pykor leadership was not only studying us but also testing Jhenda and others of their people to see if they were capable of handling future "placements."

Jhenda was given the name Ahmaad DaKunle. He was attending the University of Kwara at Kwara State, Nigeria, where he studied human medicine under the guise of becoming a doctor.

Jhenda befriended and became attached to a young man from Dakar, Senegal studying urban planning at the same university. His name was Nayeke LaVoile. They had been dating for about two years before Jhenda was killed. I was able to speak to Jhenda's taecs (parents) and learned that they never met his tjoka kdre (linked soul–boyfriend) but hoped to at the end of Jhenda's mission was that Nayeke would return to Pykor.

Once there, they would be able to prolong his life so he lived as long as any Pykor. However, before that could happen, things on Earth unraveled like threads on old tattered clothes. The exact date was June 7, 2183.

I struggle to think about what I saw humans do and what happened to them before my eyes. The horror was like the legendary tsunamis of the early 21st century hitting the entire planet in waves. My heart felt raw as if someone were holding it in their bare hand. Two, maybe three weeks before our planet was annihilated a US space shuttle was in route to deliver supplies and switch workers on the moon colony it was developing. They spotted a small Pykor ship about 250 miles above the moon's surface. The shuttle was one of the newer models and the shuttle team was given the green light from NASA military division to pursue the craft.

The Pykorians were not afraid and simply looked at this incident as the opportunity to make open contact with the human species. The shuttle's crew was able to maneuver the Pykor craft so that it was near the inter-continental space station that was completed more than one hundred years earlier. They eventually got them to dock and go aboard the space station.

The Pykorians were hesitant at first but eventually decided it was time we knew who they were, and to let us know they had been observing us for more than two centuries. So, they told everything about who they were and why they were in our solar system to the scientists on the station representing various countries. This information was relayed to each government. They also recalled most of their people living on Earth but allowed some to remain so that humans would not fear what they could not see or interact with. All were excited and yet cautious back on Earth. But as usual, there are always at least one person or group that wants more than it deserves.

Maybe a week later, the US government enacted a scheme to kidnap a Pykorian and ransom the individual for technological information. The US kidnapped approximately thirty of their people in order to force the Pykorians to comply with their demands so they'd have an advantage over others. The Pykor were more disappointed than angry.

The US government was still feeling threatened by the growth of nations previously considered third world or developing countries. NASA and the federal government planned to use the information to take the lead in colonizing Mars and Saturn.

The Pykorian leaders refused to give the US anything and hoped the government would come to its senses. Instead, military war-mongers decide to kill one-third of the captive Pykorians to show them how serious they were, about getting the technology. They murdered them by blowing up the facility they were being held in. If they didn't get the information requested, they made it clear they would kill the rest of their people.

They Pykorians wasted no time in reacting by retrieving the remaining hostages through a portal transportation system I learned about much later. It works on the principle of creating small holes in space that are controllable. Once they had all the rest of their people it was days before we heard anything else from the Pykorians. Many in the world and the news media felt that the US should apologize for its actions that marred the first true extraterrestrial contact known to man.

In fact, several governments in European, Africa, Asia and South America, threatened them with reprisals if they did not make amends immediately. Time passed as if we lived in a vacuum. No sound, movement, or a word from the Pykorians for a week. When they did, all the little boxes and the little minds living in them around the world collapsed. No insurance companies would be called for help to rebuild, FEMA would not have to worry this time because there would be nothing to rebuild.

The phone rang around 5:00 a.m. at my shop on the day the Pykorians finally responded to the massacre of their people. I had fallen asleep at my store after finishing a project I hoped to sell at the local artist's market.

"Hello, who ..., who's calling?" I said in a sleepy voice.

"Terrell, wake up man, and turn on the television to Free Speech TV quick!" returned an anxious and scared voice from the other end.

"Kamaal is that you? Why are you calling so early, is everything alright?" I said scared by his fear.

"The Pykorians have answered, and it looks like they are... man, just turn on the television, quick before it's all gone."

My heart began to bang on my chest like the police knocking on the door of a suspect.

"Hold on okay?" I demanded as I got up and went to the back room where the TV was at.

I quickly turned to the station dreading what I was going to find. It was a nightmarish scene of Washington, DC. The White House was burning wildly out of control and more than two-thirds of it was charred and in rubble. The main entrance was the only thing that was standing somewhat normally. People were running frantically through the streets and a male reporter was in tears trying to relay the story of destruction to the audience. At that moment, a woman walked in front of the camera and started pulling out her hair screaming, "God is punishing us, God is punishing us for all our sins! Are you ready to be judged?"

And like a light bulb shedding light just when you needed it, I remembered these words I read from the

157

old book called the Bible; a book forgotten by most of us, along with all the other books like it.

> "And I say unto you, that many shall come from the east and west and shall sit down with Abraham, and Isaac, and Jacob, in the kingdom of heaven. But the children of the kingdom shall be cast out into outer darkness: there shall be weeping and gnashing of teeth - Matthew 8:11-12"

"Damn Kamaal, this is real, they are going to destroy us all," I said in a little boy's voice. I did want my mother, but breast cancer had taken her from me four years earlier.

"Don't change the channel. Wait until you see where else they have already hit," Kamaal responded.

The scene changed to the Pentagon where there was only a smoldering imprint of the building on the ground and the Capitol building's dome was lying in the street like a broken egg. It was as if they wanted us to suffer by watching the nation being picked apart piece by piece.

"We have just confirmed that the President and Vice President of the Unites States and their families are dead and that the military has taken control of the country. General Kurtrick Blade has ordered a nuclear strike against the Pykorians and activation of the Satellite Laser Defense program in an effort to counteract their measures against us," came the same reporter from earlier. This was all surreal to me at this point.

The camera scene changed to a scene from outer space above the planet where the Laser Defense was firing at will against the large ship in orbit. It looked like a laser light show at a local planetarium. The ship was similar to the one that was spotted near the then moon, but seven times larger. I almost had a feeling of hope in my stomach, but it was quickly shattered when the Pykorian's ship sent out a blast that disintegrated the laser defense with one blast. In an instant, the space above the planet was almost free of any signs of human technology.

"Terrell, baby, you still there…Terrell!?" asked Kamaal.

"Yeah, baby, I'm here. Just in shock, I guess."

I changed the channel to FSTV and they had shots of several nuclear missiles being launched into space. Before they could reach the outer atmosphere, they were somehow turned around back toward the Earth in various directions. One hit California and another Miami on the East coast and then others were deflected to Eastern Europe. It was as if they were directing them toward places that would cause the most damage. The one that hit the West coast caused the California to break away from the rest of the continental USA.

Nevada was under a huge cloud of nuclear death and the nation was hopeless. I realized after about twenty minutes Kamaal and I hadn't said a word. I could hear him breathing, the same steady low rhythm I was used to when we could spend nights together. I wished at the moment we were holding each other; because I had the painful feeling, we would never see each other again.

"I love you, Terrell," he said reading my mind.

"I love you back and more," is what I always said. But I couldn't seem to move from in front of the news and I know Kamaal was feeling the same.

More reports were coming in from around the country and the world of the total and complete destruction of human civilizations. By this time the sun was coming up on the nation, but it was clear that our lives were setting in the horizon.

The satellite transmissions of all stations worldwide were interrupted by a message from the Pykorians.

> " In an hour and a half, we will obliterate the planet's surface of all life for its violence against us. We tried without success to understand your kind and to work to help you to see the potential in yourselves beyond the greed, lies, and hatred that infests everything that you do. We will randomly select 144,000 of humanity to take with us so that you are not completely erased

*from the cycle of existence. There will be no other
messages."*

And there was more I recalled from studying. I
remembered from my grandmother's bible these passages,

"Then I looked, and there before me was the
Lamb, standing on Mount Zion, and with him
144,000 who had his name and his Father's
name written on their foreheads. And I heard
a sound from heaven like the roar of rushing
waters and like a loud peal of thunder."
Revelation 14:1-3

My mind was shouting to my body to jump out of the window.
"I'm coming over to your place," I finally said. "I want to be
there with you while we wait."

Kamaal didn't respond right away, but finally in a soft
voice, "Be careful getting here. I'm looking out my window and
people have started going out into the streets. Some are just
walking around aimlessly and a few have started fighting with
neighbors."

"It will take me about twenty minutes if there's not too
much traffic on the way," I said throwing on some clothes while

talking. "You do still have the shotgun and .44 you bought?" I asked Kamaal.

"I have them right next to me," he responded quickly and seriously on the heels of my question. I snatched my keys and a picture of us that we took on vacation to Puerto Rico about several years ago in the city of Loiza. The streets around my place were not that bad but as I got closer to Kamaal's house it got more congested with cars and people just hanging out on the streets and in cars. Most looked like they were numb, and had a glaze over their eyes that reminded me of mental patients pumped full of calming drugs. I saw a group a high school aged kids actually laughing with one another.

A few I recognized from the strip where my shop was at where they would come and hang out. I looked over and at them and two of them nodded and another threw up a hand to recognize me. I felt sorry for them because they were good kids who would not see adulthood nor the future of their dreams come true. I slowed to see them better and noticed they were smoking the fattest blunts I had seen in a while. I had to stop, to my fear and dismay, because there was an accident ahead on the street. As I waited nervously, I didn't notice that one of the young brothers walked up to my car and tapped on the window. It startled me. He held up what looked like about an ounce of weed in a mini zip lock bag and motioned for me to lower my window. As I did, he said, "This is a going away gift for you bro. You were one of the few store owners that didn't make us feel like we were a nuisance. "Thanks," I said, wanting to cry, but I didn't want to make it harder for any of us than it already was.

"What's your name young blood?" I asked fighting to keep it all under control.

"Earl," he said as he put the bag in my hand and held it a few seconds.

"I'm Terrell", I said through a crooked smile. We left it at that and I continued on my way to Kamaal's house.

I was three blocks away and I had to dodge turned over cars and street mobs of various people fighting each other with bats, sticks, and fists, so I sped up when I heard gunfire. Before turning the last corner to Kamaal's block there was a man sitting on the curb of the street crying, beating his chest, and barring down so hard on his teeth that several of them broke in his mouth. I was so amazed by it that it took the blaring noise of the truck behind to get me to finish on my way to Kamaal's house.

As I pulled into his driveway, I noticed it had taken me about thirty-seven minutes to get there and only left us about twenty-three minutes with each other. But I was not sad because in the years we had together we had done more and become closer than most married couples who'd been together twenty years. I jumped out my car and headed for the front door that was opening as I approached it. Kamaal slammed it behind me and I waited a few minutes while he locked it. It released a lot of anxiety just to see him. And we hugged and kissed, without any useless words. He was only a couple inches taller and as I looked into his eyes, as his body started to fade and I lost the touch of his arms around my waist.

His house was replaced by the strange surroundings of what I soon knew to be the inside of the Pykorian ship. It was brightly lit, but dark in color everywhere I turned.

There were other people there and some Pykorians. The se- lection of the 144,000 who would be redeemed had begun and I was one of the lucky.

"Then shall two be in the field; the one shall be taken, and the other left. Two women shall be grinding at the mill; the one shall be taken, and the other left. Watch therefore: for ye know not what hour your Lord doth come." **Matthew 24:37- 42**

But I was without Kamaal; so, suddenly that I panicked. I ran to a window which gave a view of the Earth below the ship and I cried bitter tears of a child left behind by its mother. Knowing even amongst other humans I would be alone and afraid, all over again. I lost control and banged my head on the window until blood ran down my forehead like a shower and the earth turned red before my eyes. I don't remember what happened after that, I was hoping to be dead.

I eventually woke up with a blue face looking down into mine. I quickly remembered what had happened and why I was lying in what appeared to be a hospital of some sort on their ship. I was unsuccessful this time.

Then one Pykorian who was a distance from me came closer and said to me, "If you destroy yourself, who will be here for him?"

I looked in the direction they were pointing and there was Kamaal standing about six feet away from me looking wounded and worried. He ran to me and jumped in the bed where I was and hugged me as hard as he could, and kissed my wound tenderly. He would explain later that they teleported him when it was apparent to them I would not last without him. They also believed my craftsmanship would be helpful in creating a new world that humans could function in and feel like home.

This is how we all came to be living on our new home planet which was in fact not new at all. They had burned our planet's surface killing all remaining life and aided in its rebirth into a new kingdom that included 144,000 humans, and the remaining Pykorians from Mzyloria.

Their numbers had dwindled to about three hundred thousand. We named our new home Tyria. It helped that the

Pykorians were able to use their own knowledge of our biology to increase the life span of humans more than ten times the usual life expectancy. The seven hundred years I have lived since that day. I miss some things about the old planet, but most I do not. It is a terrible commentary on humanity that we could not get to enlightenment on our own, but I am just glad we are here now.

When they transported me to the ship back then, I still had the marijuana on me. It had enough seeds which enabled us to grow and plant it in the soil our new home. Instead of marijuana or weed, Kamaal and I call it Earl after the beautiful young brother who gave it to me. When we smoke on our trips from planet to the planet, there is no sadness, only fond memories, and living in the future mankind envisioned a millennia ago. We didn't get here, how scientists and engineers thought we would but, we are here now.

*Adinkra Symbols – come from the Asante people. The language from which the adinkra symbols derive their names, is Twi.

**Crunk – A form of hip-hop music that is centers on violence among Black males.

Orlando Taylor

ACKNOWLEDGEMENTS

It would be a sin against my ancestors if I didn't recognize all the friends and family whose relationships indirectly are a part of this work. These stories are not only of my brothers and sisters but also those people who intersected my life in an impactful manner. This first collection of poems is a culmination of my life to this point and the influences of the people in my life on my thoughts and my spirit. Many years ago, I read an old interview with Maya Angelou, and paraphrasing, she said the many of the poems of the greatest poets are mediocre. Therefore, don't let fear of what others think of writing stop you. So, that's what I tried to do with this collection and the next if I am so lucky to share more of my thoughts with others.

Orlando Taylor

Orlando Taylor is author of many poems that have been included in several anthologies such as *Blues Arrival: Stories of the Queer Black South and Migrations*, and online poetry blog sites. He is currently working on several ideas for film, television, print.

Made in the USA
Monee, IL
10 January 2023

23351381R00105